YOUR
MIND
CAN
CURE

Anita Stevens, M.D.,

and Lucy Freeman

HAWTHORN BOOKS, INC.
W. Clement Stone, Publisher
New York

CONTENTS

YOUR
MIND
CAN
CURE

1

"THE WHOLE OF THINGS"

Socrates once told the physicians of Greece that they were ineffective because they did not know the body could not be cured without taking the mind into consideration. About this same time in history, 300 B.C., Hippocrates, the father of medicine, maintained, "In order to cure the human body, it is necessary to have a knowledge of the whole of things."

Eighteen centuries later, the German physician Paracelsus wrote: "True medicine only arises from the creative knowledge of the last and deepest powers of the whole universe; only he who grasps the innermost nature of man can cure him in earnest."

Today, psychiatrists are studying the "innermost nature of man," realizing that body and mind are inseparable, physical illness and emotional conflict irreparably intertwined. Though intellectually we may try to separate them, emotionally we cannot, any more than we can stop our heart from beating or our lungs from breathing.

Emotions are the cause of most physical distress. There is no organ of the body, no system of the body, that may not be affected by emotional conflict. The ills accompanying mental anguish are found literally from head to toe and from the inner lining of the intestinal tract to the outer layer of skin covering the body.

Over the years patients have come to me with every conceivable physical illness, both when I was a specialist in the treatment of the skin and allergies and, more recently, in my role as a psychiatrist. Almost every ailment could be traced to emotional conflicts, many of which had been denied since childhood and were activated by current problems. In fact, it was my growing awareness as an allergist that the underlying causes of such specialized complaints were emotional that led me to become a psychiatrist. In my psychiatric practice with men, women, adolescents, and children, I have discovered what I learned in theory —that all physical illnesses are closely connected to personal problems and internal stress.

Even when we allow ourselves to become fatigued and vulnerable to illness, we are manifesting a signal of psychic distress that will not permit us to get enough sleep or take care of ourselves so that we will not fall ill.

A positive attitude about ourselves and our ability to solve our conflicts not only helps keep them under control but also tends to decrease our physical illnesses since the processes of body and mind are so interwoven.

Tension, depression, mourning, fear of sexual desire, fear of hostile impulses, all may become converted into illness in any part of the body. Physical illness, in a sense, is the way our body helps out when our psyche becomes overburdened with conflicts. Sexual conflicts, for instance, may play an important role not only in the overt symptoms of impotence and frigidity but in the repression of wishes whose denial may lead to ulcers or migraine headaches.

When we fall physically ill, we are telling of concealed wishes, including the wish to be cared for and loved, the wish to retreat from the world of reality temporarily, and the wish to express feelings we dare not consciously admit. We could spare ourselves much physical suffering throughout life if we were able to look within ourselves more honestly. Sometimes this is difficult to do without the help of a psychiatrist because we are taught to bury deep our strongest desires in order that we may be "civilized."

For centuries man believed the "devil" caused physical sickness. Then, as the science of medicine started to make headway, it was believed that "constitutional factors" were responsible— the body and its inherited deficiencies were to blame.

At the turn of the twentieth century, Sigmund Freud discovered a new way of thinking about physical, as well as psychic, illness. For the first time in mankind's history, Freud showed that the psychic mechanisms involved in falling psychically ill could also cause physical illness.

He demonstrated how a paralyzed arm could be the result of "paralyzed" emotions. How a headache could reflect the wish not to think about something believed dangerous to the self-esteem. How blindness could represent the wish not to see something regarded as obscene and evil.

Freud also discovered the way of reaching hidden emotions so physical illness could be eased. As a result of his work, and of the many investigators who followed, today it is accepted by most of the medical profession that physical illness is the way our body may respond to an emotion or thought we believe menaces our psychic survival.

Sometimes we are aware of what we are thinking and feeling. At other times we are only dimly aware of it. On occasion it is only a fleeting thought or feeling, quickly dispatched to the lower depths of our mind. And sometimes we are completely unaware of the feeling or thought.

Psychiatrists call the illness, whether it be earache, stomachache, headache, or ulcer, a "symptom." The symptom is the surface eruption of the buried feelings that are causing distress and seeking some outlet. The symptom is one way of discharging anxiety aroused by hidden feelings tied to some wish that is forbidden fulfillment by our conscience.

A symptom may reflect not only reality but also fantasy. In other words, if you imagine you are being poisoned, this may cause the same reaction in your body as though you *were* poisoned. There have been instances in which a man bitten by a snake he believes to be poisonous dies—but from a heart attack caused by fear, for it is later discovered the snake was not poisonous.

No one has to take the word of Freud and other psychoanalysts that emotions may cause bodily illness. For a famous nonpsychoanalytic, Dr. Walter B. Cannon, showed that the direct expression of psychological states could produce physical symptoms. He proved, through tests on human beings, that emotions—particularly rage—caused profound changes in the blood chemistry. These changes were principally due to the production of sugar by the activity of the adrenal glands. Disturbances also occurred in the respiratory and circulatory systems and gastrointestinal tract. Cannon measured changing units of hydrochloric acid secreted by the stomach, variations in blood pressure shown in the mercury columns of blood pressure machines, and disturbances in the rhythm of the heartbeat as pictured by the electrocardiogram.

He proved that when a flood of anxiety pours into the brain's higher cortical centers—those that control our conscious thinking—the anxiety may paralyze these centers. Then the subcortical centers, our autonomic nervous system, go into action as kind of a substitute director. However, it reacts in a rigid pattern because it is not subject to "will" but is automatic. It is governed by our primary thinking system, which means it gives symbolic, rather than direct, expression as an outlet for the repressed emotions the conscious has been unable to handle.

The changes that take place form emotional stress independently of what we call "willpower." Thus, the body's reaction to fight or flee from a dangerous situation occurs whether the emotion causing the changes is conscious or unconscious.

In her classic book on psychosomatic medicine, *Emotions and Bodily Changes*, Dr. Flanders Dunbar cited "two errors" that she said were common in trying to understand the causes of physical illness: (1) confounding the physiological mechanisms through which the psyche operates with the fundamental cause of the illness, (2) assuming that a psychological cause must be a conscious conflict.

The psychic causes of physical illness are usually unconscious. If they were conscious, there would be no need to fall ill, for we could consciously handle the conflicts. The physical symptom usually can be traced back to experiences once conscious but now unconscious and repressed from awareness. Reconstruction of the psychic structures of organic disturbances, regardless of whether they are so-called organic diseases (supposedly stemming from physical causes) or organ neuroses (stemming from psychological causes), shows again and again that the organic symptoms, as well as their meaning and tendencies, have the same origin as the psychic symptoms of a neurosis.

Dr. Felix Deutsch, a pioneer in psychosomatic studies, wrote that "with every experience which cannot be assimilated a part is converted into the organic sphere." He conducted experiments that showed that the suggestion of somatic symptoms under hypnosis, when the person had no recollection of the experience that produced the symptoms, resulted in bodily symptoms. But once the experience was remembered consciously, the same suggestion under hypnosis failed to produce physical illness.

Calling attention to a "too common unwillingness among physicians to regard seriously the emotional elements in disease," Cannon played a key role in the investigation of the relation of emotions to the nervous system and disturbances of bodily function. His classic book, *Bodily Changes in Pain, Hunger, Fear, and Rage,* published in 1929, described his research into the relationship of feelings and changes within the body.

In trying to find out which part of the brain controlled emotion, Cannon reviewed the evidence that the thalamus was concerned with the emotional aspect of sensation, and the viscera (our internal organs) were controlled only at the thalamic level, whereas skeletal muscles were governed at both levels, cortical (conscious thinking) and thalamic (unconscious).

The thinking part of our mind—the cortex—cannot cause, nor can it prevent, the intense, violent emotions that increase the blood sugar in the body, or step up the processes of the heart, or interfere with our digestion. When we feel a deep emotion, we can repress it, but only in its outward expression. It will still have an effect on our bodily processes.

For instance, an employer speaks harshly to his secretary, calling her "stupid" because of an error she made, not taking into consideration that everyone is entitled to a few errors. The secretary feels like hitting back at her boss, both physically and in verbal assault, but bites her tongue and says not a word and makes no hostile move. She has repressed all outward expression of her emotion. But that does not mean it has disappeared. Its effect is now channeled to various parts of her body. Her heartbeat may accelerate. She may feel like vomiting. Or the blood sugar in her body may rise.

An emotion, if repressed, does not disappear but finds substitute, partial gratification in some other part of the body. This means that, dismissed by our conscious, or cortical, control, the emotion falls under the domination of the thalamus, which controls the unconscious part of the mind.

This is why, in many instances, it is of little use to try to argue a patient out of his emotional reactions, since the cortex, or his reason, has no direct control over the unconscious thoughts that dominate so much of his behavior. Those hidden feelings that are the source of this conflict must be brought to his awareness. This is what happens during psychoanalysis when physical symptoms clear up as the unconscious conflicts that caused them become conscious.

A young girl who was very shy and found trouble defending herself when she was attacked verbally by her friends came to me for help because of severe stomach upsets. During her treatment, she soon became aware of how she held back all expression of her angry feelings but they found an outlet through her stomach cramps. As she was able to talk back to those who caustically attacked her with words, her stomach cramps disappeared.

Cannon believed that emotional expression resulted from the action of subcortical centers (the unconscious) and that thalamic processes were a source of emotional experience. He said, "The peculiar quality of the emotion is added to simple sensation when the thalamic processes are roused." Our conscious feeling about an emotion results in the interaction between the processes of our thalamus, the seat of our primitive feelings, and our cortex, the thinking part of our mind. Though not too much is known about it as yet, there exists what scientists call the limbic system, a kind of message center that facilitates the exchange between the thalmus and the cerebral cortex.

For instance, a sensation of wishing to fight someone may occur in the thalmus and is then relayed through the limbic system to the cerebral cortex which, in light of our past experiences, decides what to do—whether to accept, modify, or reject the wish. The limbic system makes possible the exchange of primitive emotion in the thalamus and the controls exerted on our emotions by the cortex, or our logical mind.

Cannon originated the word "homeostasis," referring to bodily functions. He explained:

> The coordinated physiological processes which maintain most of the steady states in the organism are so complex and so peculiar to living beings—involving, as they may, the brain and nerves, the heart, lung, kidneys, and spleen, all working cooperatively—that I have suggested a special designation for these states, *homeostasis*. The word does not imply something set and immobile, a stagnation. It means a condition—a condition which may vary, but which is relatively constant.

Dr. Hans Selye, author of *The Stress of Life*, is another nonpsychoanalytic scientist who has described the effect of psychological stress on the body. Both his work and Cannon's give evidence that changes caused by emotions can affect *every cell in the body*. Dr. Selye studied the effect on the body of cortisone, or ACTH, an adrenal gland hormone extracted from ox bile or prepared synthetically from certain tropical plants, used in the treatment of rheumatic fever, rheumatic arthritis, ulcers, gout, asthma and bursitis, and at times for allergies and malignancies. ACTH increases the output by the adrenal glands of other hormones, however, including androgen, which, doctors warn, may not be desirable. The effects vary considerably and must be carefully weighed in every patient against the widespread effects on each part of his body.

For instance, at one time it was thought ACTH might be useful in combating mild mental illness, and it was given to neurotic patients to calm them down. But it had the opposite effect, creating a psychotic break in some, so its use in this area was promptly stopped.

The body is not just the sum of its parts. For psychic processes are involved in its movements, giving a certain quality to the way we act and think. These mental processes are governed by what Freud called "the principle of constancy." The psychic processes strive to maintain an equilibrium in the mind so that it is free for conscious thought.

The "principle of constancy" governs the operation of our psyche. This is very important to remember in a discussion of the relation between bodily ills and emotional conflicts.

To understand how an emotion may be transformed into a physical illness requires explanation of the mental process Freud called conversion.

The mental processes are characterized by energy and activity just as are the physical processes. The difference is that you cannot see the activity of your mental processes. But you *feel* the results as, for instance, you gradually become tired, you get a sudden burst of creativity, you decide to go to one movie rather than another, or you break a date you do not wish to keep.

As the first step in the mental process of conversion, one of our psychic processes called repression goes into operation. We "repress," or relegate to the unconscious part of the mind, something we believe painful or dangerous to self-esteem. It may be the wish to strike someone who has insulted us, the wish to have sex with someone who belongs to another, the wish to masturbate, the wish to have physical relations with a member of the same sex.

The aim of the unconscious psychic process of repression is to weaken psychic pain, to take away from the thought some of its emotional force. The process of repression does so by diverting the psychic energy attached to the wish into some channel of the body where it will not be felt so intensely. The organ affected is somehow related to the buried thought.

Thoughts never vanish. No thought is ever lost to the unconscious, which stores it forever. Sir Charles Scott Sherrington, Nobel Prize winner in physiology, showed that in the case of two reflexes seeking a common pathway of expression, with only one able to get it, the other just bided its turn and occurred as an "after-discharge." The energy of the inhibited reflex did not disappear but persisted in undiminished strength, waiting to take effect later. In other words, a drive, temporarily inhibited, has by no means renounced its goal of satisfaction but simply postponed it to a more favorable time. Or, as Freud discovered, if denied an outlet, the drive had to be satisfied with partial expression in some organ of the body.

But then at least the dangerous or embarrassing thought is not conscious, where we would have to struggle so hard against it that we would be unable to think of anything else. If we did not have the ability to repress, we would probably never move out of our bed in the morning. Life would be too tough.

Thus a thought, either conscious or unconscious, can produce a change in the body. Memories and emotions "do not work in a vacuum," as Dr. Calvent Stein in his book *Nothing to Sneeze At* puts it. They operate throughout the body and especially through the sympathetic or "autonomic" nerves. He describes the autonomic nervous system as "an accessory nervous system that is like the automatic signalling devices on our railways." A familiar example is the "solar plexus" or celiac ganglion in the pit of the stomach—a blow to which can be fatal, as with boxers.

Stein calls the autonomic nervous system "a gigantic secret service which has agents (nerves, hormones, ganglia or nerve

switchboards, and glands) and operates silently, swiftly, and effi-
ciently all over the body." He adds, "It is largely on its own, but
is in cahoots with our emotions and reports to headquarters (the
conscious mind) in its own good time. It also uses a secret code,
which our conscious mind may be unable to decipher. The code
is represented by our 'neuroses,' that is, by our psychosomatic and
psychovisceral or 'functional' nervous disorders—complaints for
which no apparent organic or structural causes can be found.
These coded messages are our traffic warning signals. Like our
great naval operations, the months of planning and preparation
for which are unknown to us until *after* the assault has begun, our
neuroses are often well established before we are aware of them."

He goes on to state, "In life, many criminals think they are
getting away with things until they are caught. Our neuroses are
the unconscious penalties which we pay for our emotional
'crimes,' most of them imagined."

Hypnotism has borne out the truth of conversion. For instance,
a man who suffered arthritis so severely in his right arm that he
could not raise it went to a hypnotist seeking to be cured. The
hypnotist told him, while he was in a trance, that when he woke
he would find nothing wrong with his arm. The man, on awaken-
ing, found his arm normal. He thanked the hypnotist and went
home. The next morning he got out of bed, went into the kitchen,
seized a large knife, walked back to the bedroom, and plunged the
knife into his wife's heart.

He hated her intensely and had been repressing the wish to kill
her for years. She was a dominating, selfish woman whom he was
unable to leave. Instead, he paralyzed his right arm via arthritis
to keep from expressing intense rage, one that eventually drove
him to murder her. The physical illness—the arthritis—had weak-
ened the emotional force of his wish. But the hypnotist's suggestion that his arm was normal, which he accepted, had restored
emotional force to the wish to kill. Once the bodily symptom, his
arthritis, had vanished, the wish overpowered his conscious
thoughts.

This is an extreme example, but it shows the purpose of the process of conversion—to ease psychic pain. This man had turned his hatred on his own body, destroying one of its functions, rather than kill his wife as he so intensely wished to do, and rather than leave her, which he could not do because of his dependence on her. He was inflicting suffering on himself, both physically and psychically, because of an inability to grow up emotionally.

Our life is governed by our wishes, both conscious and unconscious. It is the wish that comes first, then the mind decides what to do about it—whether to act on it or reject it. We cannot move without the wish propelling our body into action. When we wake in the morning, we must first wish to get up before we can move our limbs from the bed. Then we must wish to get dressed before we can put on clothes, wish to have breakfast before we can eat.

The wish upsets the "constancy" of the mind. Like a storm-driven wind stirring a field of wheat, the wish arouses tension in the psyche. This tension must be resolved, either in the carrying out of the wish or distributing its energy elsewhere, so that equilibrium may be restored to the psyche. Unless the tension is eased, the psyche will be overwhelmed by stimuli from within and without and cannot function. Or it will function poorly, which is what happens in psychosis.

In the interest of survival, our psyche is always prepared to combat outer danger, which for the most part it fights successfully. Our eyes see a man with a gun running toward us, and we dash into a nearby building to escape hurt or possible death. Our ears hear the horn of a speeding car as we walk across the street, and we run to the sidewalk to avoid being struck.

But the dangers inside us are not as easy to flee. We may be seized with a sudden wish to strike someone who has insulted us. If we carry out the wish to strike, we may harm, if not actually destroy, the other person. So we repress the wish to strike him. The natural discharge of psychic energy attached to that wish—action—is blocked.

Then what happens? The energy of the psychic wish must find

some discharge in order to restore "constancy" to the mental processes of the mind. One way is through physical illness. The wish to kill, which has been a conscious feeling for a moment, is now consigned to our secondary, or autonomic, nervous system, which controls the functions of the body. It takes over the delegation of the psychic energy which it assigns to some part of the body that will serve as partial outlet for the wish.

The loss of conscious control over an organ is a detrimental substitute-information for the miscarried repression, in the words of Freud. It is only possible at this cost. But it is a lesser cost than if we had carried out the original wish, which in this case might mean murder and the giving up of our own life for having committed that murder. Our unconscious system uses an organ of the body as an outlet for the partial, symbolic gratification of a wish. In a sense, we kill ourselves a little to prevent ourselves from actually killing someone else.

For instance, a woman came to me with an outbreak of skin rash which she could not seem to get rid of. During her analysis she revealed a strong unconscious desire to masturbate—the result of feeling unloved by any man—which she had repressed for years. Instead of touching herself in forbidden places, she scratched the irritating rash, in displacement of the area she really wanted to "touch."

Thus does a strong wish change a bodily state. But there is still the question as to why a particular organ is affected. Why does one person suffer from poor vision? Another fall ill of a heart attack? A third get ulcers? A fourth, cancer? A fifth, diabetes?

Psychoanalysts believe the answer lies in the erotic and aggressive experiences of the person affected and his reaction to them. His life must be studied carefully in terms of his erotic and aggressive fantasies in order to determine why he has poor vision, has suffered a heart attack, or is ill of ulcers, cancer, or diabetes.

It is possible that the organ or organ system that becomes diseased is the one that, in fantasy, has become what Freud called erotized, the part on which sexual tension has been displaced.

That is, the organ is connected in a symbolic way to the wish to fulfill erotic yearnings believed taboo.

For instance, one fifty-year-old woman came to me after she had undergone a hysterectomy for an enormous tumor. She kept referring to the tumor as her "phantom baby." During her analysis it was revealed that she had never been able to break her too-close attachment to her father. She had not married, though she had undergone an abortion when she was thirty. The tumor represented, as she told me, half in jest, her "phantom baby," the father of whom, in her fantasy, was her own father, a tabooed father. Thus were explained the abortion (how could she bear a baby when the father was her own father, in her fantasy?) and the symbolic significance of the tumor.

In other words, that part of the body used erotically in fantasy as displacement for a forbidden sexual wish is the part eventually destroyed (Freud said that every excess carried within it the seeds of its own destruction). It may be, too, that the part of the body affected was the actual target of an erotic sensation in childhood. A mother may have excessively fondled her son's ears, and he associates the touch of his ear with his mother's love and forbidden incestuous desires. In later years, if he remains too attached to his mother, unable to transfer his love to another woman, he may lose his hearing or get frequent ear infections, the "eye for an eye" retaliation for his tabooed incestuous yearnings (the unconscious part of the mind acts in this primitive "eye for an eye" way of punishing the self).

Or a child may be excessively exposed to the sight of his parents' nude bodies, a sight that arouses him sexually and creates feelings he does not know how to handle. In later years, if he is unable to break free emotionally of his seductive parents, he may develop poor vision, as though shutting out sight of what originally excited him and aroused strong desires that terrified him.

If the respiratory system is affected, it may be that "breathing" has served as an outlet for erotic wishes, with the respiratory system overused and overabused in the service of fantasies, so that

eventually it breaks down, in part or in whole. Or if the throat
has been important in the erotic fantasy life of the person,
overused and overabused, it may become cancerous or diseased in
other ways.

One must also consider the glands, which are closely connected
to sexuality and which both excite and inhibit sexual responses.
The glands may be an extremely important factor in assigning,
through fantasy, our psychic energy to certain organs that represent sexual activity that has been inhibited but at least is now
afforded partial outlet. Just as half a loaf is better than none, so
a partial outlet for a powerful impulse is better than no outlet at
all. For as we have seen, if the energy were turned back on the
conscious mind, the mind would soon become confused, chaotic,
senseless.

Freud maintained that all psychic events are primarily conditioned by "drives," or instincts, and that the two strongest drives
are the aggressive (which is concerned with the preservation of
self so we may survive) and the erotic, or sexual (concerned with
procreation, to make sure the species continues).

It is well to remember that the most powerful wishes that have
to be repressed deal with our aggressive and sexual impulses. We
cannot destroy all those who injure our self-esteem, nor can we
be as sexually promiscuous as we might wish. But we can learn to
"suppress" a wish, which is a conscious act, rather than "repress"
it, which is unconscious and therefore may cause physical illness.
It is the *denial* of the wish and its accompanying emotions, the
lack of awareness of what we feel, that may do bodily damage.

Emotional disturbance rests on a conflict of drives—the colli-
sion between the primitive and secondary drives (our conscious
and unconscious)—according to Freud. He described neurosis as
the result of an unsuccessful compromise between conflicting and
incompatible drives.

Psychoanalysts find regularly in the conflict of drives within a
patient that the primitive (sexual and aggressive) drives give way
to the cultural secondary drives and become repressed. During the

process of individual psychoanalytic therapy, the patient becomes conscious of these repressed primitive drives and thus frees the psychic energy bound up in the repressive forces—a veritable jailer of true feelings.

The psychosomatic approach originated in the study of disturbances of our involuntary nervous system that developed under certain emotional states. First, the normal bodily responses to emotions that serve as the physiological base of the various disturbances affecting the different organs must be understood.

The total functioning of our nervous system is aimed at maintaining conditions within us in a state of constancy, as has been pointed out. Our nervous system achieves this by the principle of the division of labor. Our voluntary central nervous system takes care of the regulation of our relations to the external world. Our autonomic nervous system controls the body's internal operations —what we call the internal vegetative processes. Our "sympathetic" nervous system is part of our autonomic system. It takes care of such functions as the storing of sugar in the liver, the contractions of the pupil of the eye as protection against sudden intense light or a blow, and coughing as protection against an irritating substance in the throat.

Our sympathetic nervous system is involved in the way we deal with "fight or flight." For instance, a woman was walking down Ninety-third Street in New York City in the darkness of early night when she noticed the street was almost deserted. Suddenly out of nowhere she saw a strange-looking man coming toward her. She sensed he could be dangerous and might have intentions of mugging her. She turned, and quickly fled in the opposite direction, toward Madison Avenue which was brightly lit and on which a number of persons strolled. As she became aware of the danger, then turned and ran, her body went through certain changes. Her heart beat faster, she had difficulty breathing, which meant her lungs were engaged in extra action, and her blood pressure rose. The physical balance of her body was upset in the interest of self-preservation.

Dr. Franz Alexander in his book *Psychosomatic Medicine* described the internal economy of the human being during the states of relaxation and reaction to danger as behaving "as a nation does in war and in peace." His account continues:

> War economy means priorities for war goods and prohibition of certain peacetime productions. Tanks are produced instead of passenger cars, munitions are produced instead of luxury goods. In the organism, the emotional state of preparedness corresponds to war economy and relaxation to peace economy, as certain organ systems which are needed in the emergency become stimulated while the others are inhibited.
>
> In neurotic disturbances of the vegetative functions, this harmony between external situation and internal vegetative processes is disturbed. The disturbance may take different forms.

In general, the emotional disturbances of vegetative functions may be divided into two main categories, he said: preparation for fight or flight in emergency, and withdrawal from outwardly directed activity.

The disturbances belonging to the first category are the results of inhibition or repression of "self-assertive, hostile impulses," he noted. Because these impulses are repressed or inhibited, the corresponding behavior (fight or flight) is never carried through. Yet the organism remains physiologically in a constant state of preparedness.

Thus, although internal automatic processes have been readied for aggressive activity, the planned activity is not completely fulfilled. However, the chronic state of readiness for action lingers in the body along with those physiological reactions required for adequate functioning in an emergency situation, such as increased heart rate, heightened blood pressure, or dilatation of the blood vessels in the skeletal muscles.

In a normal individual these physiological changes are only temporary. They last only as long as the need for increased energy persists. After fight or flight, the person feels at ease as the physiological processes return to normal. But when, following the activation of the vegetative processes involved in the preparation for action, no action takes place, the body will suffer.

In a sense, each time we fall ill our body is telling us we are unhappy because of some act we are unable to perform. We cannot, of course, act on many of our most primitive wishes because if we did, we would be "uncivilized." But if we can at least become aware of these wishes, we can better handle them. We can "choose" what to do about them, rather than being driven by them and suffering in our body.

As happens all too frequently, new sources are continually hailed as the "cause" of this or that disease. For instance, a number of illnesses were once attributed to endocrine disturbances. Now we know that endocrine difficulties may be caused by underlying emotional conflicts. Medical treatment may counterbalance an endocrine disturbance by providing a temporary antidote or by crippling the organ of expression itself, as with the removal of the thyroid. But only the treatment of the underlying emotional conflicts will eliminate the cause of the illness.

There is no escape from the impact of our strong primitive drives—except through knowledge of the self.

2

THE HEAD

In considering the body from head to toe, let us start with the topmost part—the hair. Not every illness to which man succumbs will be mentioned, for this book is not a medical encyclopedia. But diseases found in all areas of the body are cited, particularly those most prevalent.

You might think the hair on the head would be immune to psychological stress. But do we not speak of "hair standing on end" when something frightens or shocks? This happens in animals as well as humans. In a sense, the quills of the porcupine, which stand up when he senses danger, reveal his hair standing on end.

When the scalp is affected, as with any part of the body that seems for the moment to be failing, there is apt to be in our life some intolerable situation from which we are unconsciously trying to escape via the physical symptom. The symptom is usually the expression of some psychic conflict that we can solve in no other way than "flight into illness." This in itself represents an attempt at cure, even though it is one that fails.

A man in his late fifties came to my office when I was practicing dermatology in Santa Fe, New Mexico. He had a very worried expression on his face.

"Look at this," he said.

He bent his head low and showed me his scalp. There were

bare, round areas on it. This is a type of baldness known as alopecia areata. The hair falls out in rounded patches.

Psychiatrists have written about soldiers who went completely bald as their hair fell out during the crises of battle. One lost his hair two days after the explosion of a shell that nearly killed him. The hair of another fell out in circular patches following a barrage of gunfire.

I asked this man, "Have you been through any emotional upset recently?"

He looked at me in awe. "Are you psychic, Dr. Stevens? How did you know?"

"Your scalp condition could be the result of anxiety," I told him.

"Maybe you read the newspapers," he said. "What happened to me was in all the papers."

"No, I didn't read about you. Sometimes I'm so busy I don't have a chance to see the paper for days," I apologized, wondering if he had been part of some scandalous divorce. Or perhaps he had lost a loved one in a tragic accident.

"Here's what happened," he said. "First I'd better tell you that I own a curio shop where I sell jewelry, belts, and rugs made by the Indians. It's in an old adobe building. I live in the rear.

"Last Wednesday, about midnight, I was wakened suddenly by loud sounds. I jumped out of bed, looked out the window, and saw a thief coming out of my shop. He was carrying jewelry and belts. He had slung several rugs over his shoulders.

"I quickly slipped on my trousers and ran out to stop him. He had started to run, but I could see the outline of his figure in the light of the moon. So I chased him. I ran faster and faster, but it seemed the faster I ran, the faster he ran.

"Suddenly he stopped short as though I had shot him. He toppled to the ground, the Indian blankets falling all over him. I ran up to find out what had happened."

My visitor paused, then added in an anguished voice, "He was dead!" He looked as though he had murdered the thief. There was a white, drawn look about him.

"That must have been quite a shock," I said.

"I couldn't believe it! I felt as though I had killed him by chasing him. Which in a way I did. The doctor said he had died of a heart attack."

"But you were chasing him because he had stolen your property," I pointed out. "You shouldn't feel guilty about that. You didn't know he had a heart condition."

"I know," he said confusedly. "I was in the right and he was in the wrong. But it didn't seem to matter. I *felt* responsible for his death. Why, Dr. Stevens? Why?" It was a wail of agony.

At that period I was a dermatologist, not a psychiatrist. But I sensed this man needed to talk more than he needed anything else. So I saw him for several sessions during which I encouraged him to speak about his life in Santa Fe and his childhood.

He quickly uncovered a hatred for his father that he had never faced. In his unconscious the burglar who stole from him symbolized the father of childhood who, in his fantasy, had stolen from him his beloved mother. As a boy, he had wished his father dead many a time, fearing in turn he would be killed (or castrated—death and castration are one and the same in the unconscious). These feelings had been unconsciously transferred to the burglar who had stolen his precious possessions.

As he was able to talk about his deeper feelings, this man's hair grew back so that he had no more bald patches. One might say that his hair falling out was a kind of unconscious castration for causing the death of the burglar/father. The hair of the head may actually serve as the site of displacement of feelings about the genitals, which are protected by hair.

The same scalp symptom occurred in a woman who came to my office in Santa Fe because her hair was falling out in round patches.

I asked her, "Have you been through any intense emotional strain?"

She was a tall, angular woman with intense, slightly drawn

features. My question drew a surprised stare from her dark eyes. "Why do you ask?"

"This scalp symptom may be psychosomatic," I explained.

Tears came to her eyes. "I've been through a terrible ordeal," she said.

"Tell me about it."

"A few weeks ago, our little girl—she's two years old—was badly burned by the furnace in our home. There are horrible grille marks all over her tiny body."

At this time, in that part of the country, some houses were heated by furnaces set in the floor, with grilles placed over them as protection. The grilles could become very hot.

The mother was now sobbing. She kept saying, "It's all my fault. All my fault!"

"No, it isn't," I assured her. "Children have a natural curiosity. They explore everything in sight. You can't possibly watch them every minute. That's why children are involved in a lot of accidents. You mustn't blame yourself."

"You mean that?" Her tear-stained eyes opened wide.

"I most certainly do."

"Thank you." She wiped away her tears.

As she left, she said, "I'm so grateful. You don't know how much you have helped. I feel so relieved."

A week later she called to tell me that hair was growing in on the bald patches on her head. Again she thanked me profusely.

In a way, the appearance of bald spots on the scalp at a time of tragedy may symbolize an unconscious tearing out of one's hair. Some distraught people actually do this at a time of great grief and guilt.

Anxiety may affect the hair in other ways. Physicians have reported the sudden graying of the hair of a patient after a trauma, such as divorce or the death of someone loved. The hair of one woman only twenty years old turned completely white when a love affair ended with the man walking out on her, saying he had changed his mind and did not want to marry her.

One psychiatrist observed that on occasions the dark hair of a young man who was schizophrenic showed a silver white strip about an inch wide, one or two hours before the outbreak of a disturbed period. Once it stayed silver white for several days. However, as the young man progressed in therapy, his hair retained its normal color.

Dr. Fritz Mohr, a German psychiatrist, described psychic influences on the growth of the hair as "secondary sex characteristics," occurring by way of the endocrine glands, which are easily affected by fear and rage. He also reported that the psychotherapy of sexually pathological persons had altered the distribution of their hair.

Dandruff may be a sign of anxiety. The person with dandruff has a dry scalp condition caused by his nervousness. One man came to me for help because he wanted to leave his wife but was afraid to ask her for a divorce. I noticed that excessive dandruff flaked the shoulders of his very expensive suit. As he gained more confidence in himself, he was able to ask his wife for a divorce. Simultaneously I noticed the dandruff had vanished.

Moving downward from the scalp, we come to the forehead. Headaches are one of the most prevalent ways people try to combat inner conflicts. In a general sense, when you have a headache, there is something you don't want to think about. You are trying to repress thoughts and feelings that nevertheless keep nagging away inside you, causing the headache.

"One of the most baffling problems in medical therapeutics is that dealing with the treatment of headaches," wrote Dr. P. S. Graven in the *Psychoanalytic Review* in 1924. "The main reason for this lies in the failure to detect the exact etiology [cause] of headaches, and, strange to say, the causal factor, the psychic, which should most obviously, because of its frequency, force itself upon medical practitioners, is the one most neglected."

Many studies by psychiatrists have demonstrated the onset of a migraine headache just after a time of stress. Instead of expressing feelings of fear or rage or sorrow connected to the stress, the person gets a headache.

Dr. Frieda Fromm-Reichmann treated eight patients who suffered migraine headaches with intensive psychotherapy. She discovered in all of them hostile, envious impulses that they turned upon the self. Dr. Harold Wolff, a pioneer in the study of the migraine headache, stressed as personality features in the migraine sufferers their compulsiveness, ambition, excessive competitiveness, rigidity, and inability to keep up with their compulsively assumed responsibilities. This feeling of frustration resulted in tension and fatigue, precipitating a migraine headache. The attack occurred whenever the person faced a task he believed to be beyond his ability.

Most of the studies on the psychology of migraine headache mention the presence of repressed or suppressed hostile impulses. The most striking observation of psychoanalysts is the sudden end of an attack in a patient after he becomes conscious of his hitherto repressed rage and gives expression to it in abusive words.

The conclusion by various authorities that those who have difficulty expressing their rage may have an inclination toward migraine headaches is borne out by the fact that the inhibited persons, the sweet, "goody-goody" types, are commonly found among the migraine sufferers.

The headache is the most common symptom for which patients seek relief from the ophthalmologist, according to Dr. W. S. Inman, writing on "Emotion and Eye Symptoms" in the *British Journal of Psychology* in 1921. He noted that it seemed to be a common practice to wear glasses not to improve vision but to relieve headaches. However, the frequency and intensity of the headaches were not related to eyestrain but more often to intense emotional stress, he said.

Dr. Inman wrote, "I have found again and again that headache, eye ache, inability to focus upon reading or sewing or fine work, have begun at some period of emotional stress. Strangely enough, the patient is never aware of this fact and is always astonished when it is revealed."

Yet it is not so strange when you consider that the headache

serves the purpose of *denying* the feelings. It is one way of pro-
tecting the self against the pain of the awareness of the emotional
stress. There is great truth to the biblical saying "None so blind
as those who will not see," meaning "aware of" the truth.

When we consider poor vision, we might suggest that, psychologically speaking, those who unconsciously damage their vision
are trying to keep from seeing something they believe they should
not see—something they think wicked or obscene or fearful. The
forbidden object or objects are hidden in childhood memories—
perhaps the genital organs of a parent or the sight of sexual
intimacies that took place between parents.

The relation between the eyes and emotional conflicts was first
described by Freud in his article "Psychogenic Visual Disturbance according to Psycho-Analytical Conceptions," written in
1910. In speaking about such disturbances he stated that it was
"as if an accusing voice had uplifted itself within the person
concerned, saying: 'Because you have chosen to use your organ of
sight for evil indulgence of the senses, it serves you quite right if
you can see nothing at all now,' thus giving its sanction to the
outcome of the process."

Our unconscious is governed by the law of the talion "an eye
for an eye." And it is through our eyes that, as children, we see
things we are not supposed to see. Through the eyes we satisfy
our curiosity about our body and its functions and the bodies of
others.

Our eyes not only look out for signs of danger that may threaten
our lives but also take in the beauty of those we desire sexually.
They serve both our self-preservative and our procreational urges.

One day a man wearing bifocals walked into my office. He was
short and stocky, with strong facial features. Behind the glasses,
brown eyes gleamed with intelligence and alertness.

"I'm here for a funny reason," he said. "I have a deep fear of
going blind which my physician assures me is not a possibility,
according to X rays. He suggested I come to you to find out if I
am psychologically upset."

"Have you always needed glasses?" I asked.

"I have worn them ever since the age of ten," he said. "I wouldn't feel natural without them."

He was a stockbroker who had made a fortune on the market. He had recently been divorced by a wife who had fallen in love with another man. She had kept their two children, permitting him to see them whenever he wished.

As this man started to talk about his boyhood experiences during the sessions that followed over a period of eight months, he often brought up a feeling of being frightened of things he "saw." One day he told me about how he had walked into his parents' bedroom and seen them close together under the sheets. Terrified, he withdrew before they were aware of him, but he said that he had always felt very guilty about seeing them indulging in such an intimate act.

Again, he spoke of "seeing" two boys behind a barn playing with each other sexually, when he was eight years old. He talked of this in terrified fashion. I assured him, "This is not unnatural. It happens to many boys in the course of their growing up."

To him, anything sexual became frightening, yet at the same time fascinating. Unconsciously, he desperately wanted to "see," yet a strong conscience prevented him from seeing fully, not only the forbidden sexual acts but the world about him.

At the end of his therapy, as he lost his fear of his sexual feelings, he lost his fear of going blind. Later he met a woman his own age with whom he fell in love, and the last time he consulted with me he smilingly told me that they planned to marry in a few months' time.

The eyes are the target of the classical furnishment for oedipal desires. Oedipus put out both his eyes when he learned he had murdered his father and married his mother, by whom he had four children. Dr. Inman wrote in the article cited earlier, "One naturally turns for enlightenment to any psychological theory which might fit in with the facts, and it is with something of a shock that one remembers the emphasis laid by Freud upon the legend of Oedipus, who blinded himself in expiation of his unwitting offenses against his parents."

According to Dr. Inman, unconscious psychic factors are encountered by the ophthalmologist in the form of various neurotic symptoms. He says:

> Headaches, tics, insomnia, inability to concentrate attention, photophobia, flushing and watering of the eyes, neuralgia, anorexia, constipation, anemia, mental dullness, sleepiness and languor, squint, migraine, hysteria in many of its forms, are but a few of the troubles attributed directly or indirectly in modern English textbooks to eyestrain. Some American ophthalmologists have been even more extravagant in their views, and claim to have cured scores of other ills by means of glasses.
>
> The mental and emotional state of the patient has not been considered, and the possibility of this state determining the eye symptoms instead of the eye condition causing the general manifestations appears to have eluded both oculist and physician. . . . [T]he eye rarely produces other than ocular symptoms, unless the patient is emotionally unstable, and . . . he frequently is relieved, not by glasses but by suggestions or else by some adjustment of the inner life usually unknown to the oculist.

In another article, "Emotion and Acute Glaucoma," published in *Lancet* in 1929, Dr. Inman wrote:

> For many years ophthalmologists have accepted emotion as an exciting cause of acute glaucoma. My own experience has suggested that even though conscious emotion may not be present at any rate in a sufficient degree to account for the attack of glaucoma, nevertheless the onset may coincide with the anniversary of events once pregnant with emotion but now apparently indifferent or even long since forgotten. The psychological investigation of such cases might lead to a further knowledge of the mechanisms involved and so enable us sometimes to prevent the development of this very serious and painful disease by providing for the discharge of the emotion through legitimate channels.

A study of 150 children who squinted revealed that they all had parents who were extremely strict, almost oppressively so. Many of the children also were left-handed and stammered, other symptoms of parental strictness.

Psychiatrists have found that patients who have difficulty dealing with glare or bright light reported either a definite fear of the dark or could remember their attempts to overcome the fear during their childhood days.

Dr. Robert Lindner, a psychoanalyst, gave startling evidence of the connection between sexual fantasies and eye illnesses in his book *Rebel without a Cause* (bearing no relation to the movie except the title). Dr. Lindner traced a young boy's eye tic back to the time when, as a baby, he lay in a crib in his parents' bedroom, observing his father and mother in the act of sex.

Dr. George S. Derby, writing in 1930, referred to "ocular neuroses." He claimed that ophthalmologists too often dismissed or got rid of a neurotic patient with a minor change in prescription when what the patient really needed was the suggestion his "way of life" be changed rather than his eyeglasses. Dr. Derby urged that the word "eyestrain" be banished from the vocabulary, saying, "If the general public could learn that eyes are seldom strained, this would be a much happier world to live in." The eye has a large factor of safety, he said, and even excessive use does not make the eye diseased.

He told of a friend, fifty years old, who at times suffered from a paralysis of the arm for which doctors could find no physical cause. This man said one day, meeting Dr. Derby on the street, "I am going to Dr. So and So, my arm trouble has recurred. He will change my glasses and that always fixes me up."

Dr. Derby commented, "He thoroughly believed that eyestrain was the cause, and I fear that the ophthalmologist had never told him it was not."

Dr. T. H. Shastid, an ophthalmologist, writing in 1921, declared, "Sometimes a single word will banish stone blindness. I have had such a case."

It was the essayist Ralph Waldo Emerson, with his always-wise philosophy, who said, "Lenses should be fitted to a patient's nervous system as well as to his eyes."

Patients who consult ophthalmologists and are told their eyes are healthy often find this no consolation. They frequently feel even unhappier because now there is no physical cause for what they believe to be their poor eyesight. Every psychiatrist has seen instances in which complaints about poor vision disappear as the patient faces his underlying emotional conflicts.

One psychiatrist told of a certified public accountant who developed a far-sighted condition of the eyes and was fitted for glasses. During therapy this man uncovered a strong hatred of his daily work of bending over a desk reading small figures. He unconsciously hated his job, hated his boss, but lacked the courage to change occupations. As he became aware of his hatred, he was able to seek and find work as assistant manager in a bank. This was a job he felt was less taxing and far more enjoyable because he was around people rather than being shut up alone in a small office. He no longer needed glasses, as his eyes returned to normal vision.

A woman who wore bifocals to enable her to see work in front of her eyes, during therapy recalled, as a child, having seen her father naked one day coming out of a bathhouse to take an outdoor shower. She also recalled, in terror, the shock that had gone through her body at the time. As she could discuss her fear and horror, and also fascination, at the forbidden sight, she realized she had been distorting and exaggerating childhood fears all through the years. Her vision eventually returned to normal.

We must remember the dual function of the eye as described by Freud: an organ of orientation to the world and an organ for the reception of stimuli from a world of love and pleasure. There is also our belief as a child in a magic power emanating from the eye, "the evil eye," a belief that we retain in our unconscious. That the eye does have a sexual power is seen in the "magic" communication that takes place between two people who meet for the first time and, through exchange of glances, feel a deep attraction to each other.

Nervous tension may cause blurred vision. Muscular disturbances of the eyes are exacerbated by nerves that come from the brain. The twitching of eyeballs (nystagmus), the twitching of eyelids, the seeing of spots in front of the eyes, and glaucoma, which is produced by increased intraocular tension which, in turn, increases the fluid that keeps the eyes moist, all indicate the sufferer is repressing the sight of some feared or repugnant (imagined) object.

Several scientists reported experiments on the effect on retinal pressure of emotions evoked in the laboratory by such sounds as revolver shots and piercing cries. The pressure in the retina always rose at such sounds. The increase in pressure appeared to be in direct proportion to the intensity of the emotional stimulus.

Dr. Fritz Mohr in 1925 reported the clearing up after therapy of recurrent hemorrhages in the retina of the eyes of a woman teacher. The hemorrhages occurred right after her sister became psychotic. The teacher's blood pressure increased, and the eye hemorrhages took place repeatedly in spite of local and general ophthalmological treatment. They ceased only when it was possible for her to express in therapy her feelings of guilt about her sister, based on childhood experiences. Her blood pressure also returned to normal.

Dr. Mohr suggests that on the basis of what is known of the close connection between emotions and circulatory changes, it must be possible to save eyes through the psychic influencing of the secretory processes in the body. He says:

> Anyone who has experienced, as have I, the complete and permanent elimination in one hypnotic session of severe acute hay fever, with marked hyperemia of the conjunctiva, violent watering of the eyes, swelling of all the mucous membranes of the air passages, and intense dyspnea, will no longer have any doubts as to the possibility of altering psychotherapeutically such secretory disturbances.

Reading defects are also frequently emotional in origin. Only as they are considered as symptoms of inner conflicts do they clear up.

Disturbances of the nose have been the focus of many studies by psychiatrists and psychoanalysts. They find that prior to the catching of a cold, many people reveal some loss—the death of someone close, the loss of a job, separation from a loved one, the loss of self-esteem, or even the anniversary of a loss. Because of this sense of loss, the person becomes depressed and vulnerable to a cold virus. A happy person does not catch a cold.

There are, as far as is known, 113 viruses in the air that may cause a cold, and probably many more. The question then becomes, "Why, at this particular moment, does a person catch a cold?"

I find that if a patient arrives at the office saying, "I feel I am coming down with a cold," and he is able to talk about what is depressing him, as a rule he is able to prevent the cold. Once the virus takes hold, it is impossible to halt it. However, in the beginning stages, if the feelings of loss and depression can be brought to awareness, there appears no need for the cold to develop.

Intensive research has shown that chilling of the body, extreme changes in temperature, or being close to a person who has a cold will not bring on a cold. It usually develops out of an inner need to suffer.

The cold seems to be connected to an unconscious wish to cry, according to some authorities. One of my patients, a thirty-year-old woman whose mother was dying, had caught colds all her life. When I first interviewed her, she sat stoically in the chair, as though wearing a mask. She took pride, she said, in never having shed one tear.

"I'm no crybaby," she said firmly.

After several sessions, when she was able to lie on the couch and relax more, a few tears came to her eyes as she spoke of her dying mother. In a few weeks she was sobbing as though her heart would break as she talked about her unhappy childhood. Her father had walked out of the house when she was ten years old, and her mother had started to get depressed from that moment on.

After six months of therapy this young woman said to me in

surprise, "I haven't caught a cold since I started coming here. Can you imagine that?"

I replied, "Perhaps that's because you are facing some of the hidden reasons why you have had to catch colds."

The nose, like some other parts of the body, is especially suited for the displacement of sexual feelings. Both in its protruding shape and its two cavities and in the secretions it emits during the time of a cold, the nose may represent either male or female genitals. The skin is another area suitable for the displacement of sexual feelings, showing in its rashes and itches and eruptions, which require ointments applied by the touch, the need for the coveted "touch" of the forbidden sexual object, the parent of childhood, or the wish to masturbate, the touching of the self.

The nose has a dual function, to breathe through and to smell with. The sense of smell may be disturbed by inner tension. Dr. A. A. Brill, a famous psychoanalyst, in his article "The Sense of Smell in the Neuroses" (*Psychoanalytic Quarterly*, vol. 1, 1932), maintained that the study of patients proved quite clearly that smell plays a significant role in neurotic disturbances.

> It tends to corroborate Freud's assumption that the sexual life of man, which was originally regulated largely by olfaction, became subject to deep repressions when the sense of smell fell into desuetude in consequence of man's turning away from the earth.
>
> We may say that although the sense of smell has been almost completely superseded and displaced by sight and touch, it surely continues to play a part, albeit an unconscious part, in the mental life of man. . . . Odor probably unconsciously plays the same part in all love manifestations of civilized humanity as it does consciously among animals and primitives and many non-European races. . . . Odors in the form of perfumes still continue to play a great part in the feminine life of even the most civilized people.

Before man raised himself to stand on his two feet, when he crawled on all fours, he depended on his sense of smell to alert him to dangers and also to sexual objects. As man stood, he came to depend less on his olfactory sense. It has, however, remained a sensitive part of him. Animals use their olfactory sense as part of their sexual apparatus. In one experiment olfactory nerves were removed from puppies, as a result of which the adult male was unable to recognize the female and thus could not propagate. But when the eyes of rabbits were removed, this in no way interfered with propagation.

Impairments of hearing cause suffering to an estimated one out of every ten Americans, according to the Deafness Research Foundation. In this nation 400,000 people are deaf, unable to hear and understand speech.

Ear disturbances produced by obvious psychic reasons occur more often in women than men, according to studies. Several psychoanalysts have made the connection between menstruation and hearing, possibly because the menstrual period, when it first occurs, represents a threatening time in the life of the individual.

One young woman in her early twenties consulted me because she believed she was becoming deaf, though X rays showed no organic reason for the malfunction of her hearing.

I tried to get at the reasons for her fear of becoming deaf by probing carefully into her background and her relationship with her parents. Finally she told me, "I have always been afraid of my mother. She is a person who loses her temper easily. The least little thing can set her off. Now that I think about it, my childhood was marked by many instances of hearing her screams and shouts. She used to say that she controlled me with her voice."

I quickly posed a question to the young woman, who was still living at home. "Hasn't it occurred to you that that may be the reason you are afraid of losing your hearing and that you believe you actually are becoming deaf? What is happening is that you are unconsciously trying to shut out the sound of your mother's voice."

At first, she had difficulty understanding and accepting this possibility. But as we talked at greater length and analyzed more fully incidents from her past, she realized that she was trying to avoid hearing her mother's outbursts of temper by shutting out the sound of the older woman's voice. At the end of her therapy sessions, she had made a complete adjustment, her fears had vanished, and she was refusing to let her mother's screams bother her.

Psychoanalysts report in the therapy of men and women with impaired hearing that their hearing becomes normal as they are able to face their inner, buried conflicts. There are cases of soldiers suddenly going deaf during battle, a circumstance easily understood when the action involves heavy artillery barrages marked by exploding shells that bring with them frightening sounds and the threat of death or maiming, and recovering their hearing only after they are out of danger.

Mastoiditis, which usually strikes boys, can be understood psychologically if you consider the growth and swelling symbolically, as displacement of sexual fears at a time the boy feels himself coming of age and may be threatened by the intensity of his sexual desires.

A colleage of mine recently told me about the case of a nine-year-old boy who suddenly developed a mastoid in his left ear. He was so upset that his parents took him to a psychiatrist to calm him down before the operation. The psychiatrist was able to elicit from the boy his deep fears about sexual impulses that were frightening him. He told the psychiatrist he felt very guilty about the urge to masturbate.

One man of forty-five came to see me because, though he seemed to be losing his hearing, there was nothing organically wrong, according to several doctors who had thoroughly checked his ears. I asked him questions about his life. He was unhappily married and had decided to leave his wife, get divorced, and live alone.

"It will be very lonely—very quiet," he said sadly, "but I'll manage to stand it somehow."

"You don't like quiet?" I asked.

"I'm not used to it."

"What do you mean?"

"I have a wife who shouts and orders me around every minute I'm home," he said. "It's like being in an army where she is the general and I'm the only private. This has been my way of life."

"And you'll miss it," I said, understanding now why he was threatened by "quiet," out of a sense of guilt at leaving his wife.

"One gets accustomed to torment, and it seems natural, doesn't it?" He laughed grimly.

"Did you ever before find your ears slightly impaired?" I asked.

"After a few months of marriage, when I suddenly realized how often my wife raised her voice, I lost my hearing for a while. But then I guess I adjusted to her. Because I got it back and never lost it again. Until recently. After I moved away from her."

This man was caught in the conflict of wanting to hear and not wanting to hear. As he noted, he had become accustomed to the unpleasantness of his wife's loud voice giving orders. He felt guilty about leaving her, but he also wanted his freedom. It was the conflict that was causing his hearing impairment. Without conflict, there would be no illness.

The wife decided she would undergo treatment because she wanted her husband to return. She visited a psychiatrist, ultimately realized she had been a "scold," and apologized to her husband, and he went back to her.

Many deaf people refuse to wear hearing aids. They claim such aids are irritating and ugly. More likely the truth is that they really do not want to hear. I know one woman who claimed she could not hear who, nevertheless, heard perfectly whenever it was important for her to hear. She became deaf to words that bored or frightened her.

We next come to the mouth. Canker sores, which may appear in the linings of the mouth, are usually associated with anxiety. The mouth, the center of the first stage of our psychosexual development—the oral stage—is particularly vulnerable to the desire to be fed and to chew. When hungers go unsatisfied, the mouth, through various illnesses, including cancer, may tell of these desires.

The destruction of teeth as a result of unconscious conflicts has been noted in psychoanalytic literature. The extraction of a tooth may symbolize castration in the unconscious, the loss of an important part of the self. A person may unconsciously destroy his teeth through cavities by eating the wrong kind of foods, ones that create excessive acidity. Sugar, for instance, upsets the chemical balance of the mouth. Anxiety may also affect the chemical balance of the mouth, causing a type of decay that is often found along the sides of the roots.

In adults the condition most frequently encountered is due to improper cleansing of teeth and lack of home care for prevention of dental disease, which lead to excessive plaque formation under the gums and eventual loosening of the teeth. If people cared enough about themselves and their teeth, they would spend time cleaning their teeth properly and preventing this condition. In other words, a person with self-esteem will make sure that he spends the time necessary to insure against the loss of teeth and will eat proper foods to prevent the breaking down of the defensive barriers in the mouth.

Before leaving the outer surface of the face, we may consider the condition of acne which troubles so many adolescents. The sebaceous glands under the skin become overactive, stimulated by anxiety, and produce eruptions. Sometimes a boy or girl, fearful of dating members of the opposite sex, will unconsciously show these fears in the signs of acne which may be so severe they will prevent him or her from dating, thus escaping any confrontation.

There is also the condition of extra hairiness in women, on face, lip, and eyebrows, which may unconsciously symbolize their wish to be a man, since men are the hairy ones. There is an old saying that a woman whose eyebrows meet over her nose is jealous, and this may have some grain of truth in it, in the fact that she is jealous of men.

There is a condition known as tic douloureux, which was far more prevalent in the days when "hysteria" was popular. It is a very severe pain that occurs in the facial muscles. I saw a fifty-five-year-old man who had developed this condition, a trigeminal (fifth cranial nerve) neuritis. When he tried to eat, it was too painful for him to open his jaw, and he was wasting away. He came to me after someone suggested he consult a psychiatrist.

He was in such pain that I gave him a mild drug to ease his discomfort. The drug at least enabled him to eat, and he soon started talking about some of the personal problems causing his facial pain, which lessened the longer he was in therapy.

Lastly, we come to the interior of the head, the brain. Actually, the brain controls the whole body, and we cannot consider illnesses elsewhere apart from what takes place in the conscious and unconscious parts of the brain. The brain is the director of our central nervous system. The pituitary gland in the brain rules our entire metabolism.

The mind rules the body. "It's all in the mind," people said for years about physical illness, without realizing what this meant. It means that our thoughts may create our illnesses, thoughts we all too often banish to the far corners of the mind so they will not shame or frighten us, but thoughts that nevertheless will find an outlet, often taking the route of the motor pathways of the body.

Psychiatrists believe that our attitudes and our acts affect the functions of our brain. Our whole body is, as it were, "in tune with our brain," as Dr. Paul Schilder, a psychoanalyst who pioneered in psychosomatic theory, once put it.

The conditioned reflexes of our body are related to the processes of our psyche. In one experiment a positive conditioned reflex was built up in animals to a sound of 100 wavelengths. Then a negative reflex was established in the same animals to a sound of 104 wavelengths. Then the two sounds were produced at the same time. The animals became filled with panic. Some developed eczema. The conflict between whether to react to the pleasurable sound or the painful one produced physical symptoms in the animals.

The same holds true for humans. When someone experiences a conflict in choosing between pleasure and pain, physical symptoms may develop. One young woman of twenty-six, who suffered severe headaches, walked into my office one day, after I had seen her several times previously, and announced, "I have the *most dreadful* headache of my life at this moment."

"Sit down and tell me about it," I said.

She was a very attractive redhead, with wide blue eyes and an innocent look that men found attractive. In spite of twenty proposals she had counted up and told me about, she had never married. When I asked why, she said, "Who needs it?"

She told me that she found it very difficult to respond sexually to a man. She was not frigid, but she felt she had to know a man for months before she would feel attracted to him sexually (in this day and age a rare reaction). She had been brought up by very severe parents, who questioned her unmercifully every time she went out on, and returned from, a date. At the age of twenty, she had fled from them and her home in Lincoln, Nebraska, and moved to New York, where she got a job as receptionist in a television studio. There she came into contact with many young men and had constant dates.

Thus, she often had to choose between submitting to a sexual advance or rejecting it, and most of the time rejected it, only to find she incurred severe headaches.

I said to her, "There may be some connection between your severe headache today and what happened to you last night. Were you out on a date?"

"With the most attractive man I have ever known," she replied. "I know he likes me very much. He wanted to kiss me all night. But I wouldn't let him."

"Why not?" I asked.

She shrugged her shoulders. "Because I feel it isn't right. Until I get to know him better."

"So instead you get a severe headache," I commented.

"Oh? Is that why?" She looked surprised.

"I am not suggesting you should have kissed him," I said. "Only that you consider how your rejection of a pleasurable act may have caused the repression of feelings that was subsequently manifested in a headache."

"You know—I kept telling myself not to *think* about it, that if I thought about it, I would give in to him," she said almost eagerly. "Part of me wanted to kiss him, didn't it?"

"Yes, and it came into conflict with your conscience—the part that forbade you to do so."

"What *should* I have done?" she wailed.

"It isn't a matter of should or shouldn't," I said, "but of attempting to understand what you feel about this man. Whether you want to take him seriously and explore the relationship which, perhaps, might lead to marriage. Or to reject the relationship if it seems futile."

She stayed in therapy twelve months as she slowly realized how rigid and repressed she had been. She left therapy when she decided to marry this man, who had fallen deeply in love with her.

Epilepsy contains a strong emotional element, and seizures are often brought on by emotional stress. In addition, some convulsive seizures resemble epilepsy and are hysterical forms of emotional problems. Severe emotion, with its resulting vasoconstriction, might well cause a brief, sudden reduction of oxygen in the human brain which could then result in a fit. For instance, an epileptic boy, who as a child had been severely frightened by a ferocious dog, was studied in a laboratory. It was noted that he would throw a fit, showing signs of "organic" change in his brain, whenever a dog in the laboratory by chance barked so that he could hear it.

Psychoanalysts have noted the similarity between the movements of the epileptic and that of a person in the sexual act and have theorized it represents an unconscious wish to indulge in sexuality with someone taboo.

It is in the brain that our fantasies, sexual and aggressive, are stored—fantasies that may determine which part of the body will be affected by illness. In a sense, what we dream at night and unconsciously dream during the day may determine the organ that is physically affected.

We must remember that the body is governed by our wishes. A wish, the psychic component of the physical sensation of an instinct, or urge, always carries intense emotion to make sure it is carried out, or at least considered for action by the mind. If that intense emotion is deflected into motor pathways of the body, its discharge, over a long period of time, may well affect parts of the body.

The major role of physical movements consists in expressing and satisfying our psychological needs, wishes, and emotions through the discharge of nervous energy, whether it be weeping over a sad thought or laughing uproariously at a joke. And, just like body and mind, our conscious and unconscious may work together in the interest of survival when we feel threatened.

The threat may be either a danger from the outside world, such as someone rushing at you with a knife, or danger from your inner world, such as the wish to murder, which, if carried out, could bring an end to your life—either execution in retribution or imprisonment for endless years or psychic destruction by guilt. The unconscious and conscious parts of the mind react to every experience, and the reaction may set in motion physical changes that unconsciously, and in distorted form, express instinctual impulses that have had to be repressed.

If certain brain cells are stimulated, such as the ones that control vision or hearing, you experience a specific sensation in your eyes or ears due to the connection between that part of the brain and your eyes or ears. There is also a connection between a happening in the world outside and the brain. And there is a connection between an inner sensation, feeling, or thought and the brain. A perception, a fantasy, an idea, or a memory is either strongly or weakly "cathected," that is, strongly or weakly aroused and charged with psychic energy. It demands immediate discharge.

All of your thoughts are connected in chains of associated memories interwoven with one another, forming networks. Patients on the couch who "free-associate" use these chains of ideas to trace the source of a conflict. This is how they are helped to become aware of repressed feelings and thoughts and thus free valuable psychic energy that has had to be used as jailer of the repressed thoughts.

Freud's theory that the brain is the storehouse of memories was proved by a famous neurosurgeon, Dr. Wilder Penfield, and his associates at the Montreal Neurological Institute, whose pioneer discoveries are now widely accepted by science. Penfield's book *Speech and Brain Mechanisms*, written with Dr. Lamar Roberts, helped prove the unity of mind and body as it showed how memory operates in the brain.

While performing brain operations, Penfield discovered that as he used electrodes to stimulate mildly certain parts of the brain, his patients started to talk freely about some of their past experiences and how they felt at the time. This happened only when he applied the electrodes to particular places on the cortex just above the two temporal lobes. These sections of the brain, lying under the temple on each side of the head, are the locations of thought processes and memory.

The electrical stimulation causes a flow of memories. Penfield believed that since this did not occur when he stimulated other lobes in the brain, it seemed justifiable to conclude that those specific areas of the cortex "have a particular relationship to the record of experience" and the reawakening of memories tied to those experiences.

He compared the part of the brain that stores memory to a continuous filmstrip with a sound track. A person could talk about what he experienced and felt at any point in that strip.

One man remembered hearing a piano. Then he recalled the name of the song as "Oh, Marie." Then he heard a voice singing the song. One woman described how she felt while giving birth to her child. Another woman heard her small son speaking to her years before in the yard outside her kitchen and remembered also the sounds of the neighborhood. Some would describe their feelings about the past as "familiar." Others would recall them as distant and unfamiliar. But all agreed that the memory itself was more vivid than any they could voluntarily recall.

The discovery of such reactions showed the existence of a permanent recording of memories by the ganglia (masses of nerve cells serving as a center from which nerve impulses are transmitted), Penfield said. It seemed likely, he added, that a person used part of this record in his current life when challenged by new experiences. Penfield's patients did not regard their memories as a "remembering" but rather as a "hearing-again and seeing-again —a living-through moments of the past time." In a sense they experienced a double consciousness.

Each patient, Penfield said, "enters the stream of the past and it is the same as it was in the past, but when he looks at the banks of the stream, he is aware of the present as well. . . . The thread of time remains with us in the form of a succession of 'abiding' facilitations . . . it runs through the waking hours of each man, from childhood to the grave."

And this "thread of time" is molded in the pattern it forms by wishes that stem chiefly from erotic and aggressive impulses and their frustrations. Earliest man, according to anthropologists, gave in to his instinctual impulses. He slaughtered anyone who angered him, had sex with anyone he desired, be it his mother or daughter. But as man became civilized, he had to learn to repress such wishes, though occasionally the wishes would erupt and overwhelm his "better judgment." Then he acted according not to his "right mind" but to his "wrong mind," the part that contained evil, primitive urges.

Everyone carries early feelings of loss within him. The psycho-analysis of adults shows that the unconscious contains endless traces of earlier losses and deprivations that appear with special clarity in dreams, which often show wishes to restore the lost loved ones.

The current loss, like the electrodes Penfield placed in the brains of his patients, reawakens memories of earlier losses connected to each other by chains and chains of associations, which are called "emotionally organized memory traces." When something happens to you, such as a hurt, it stirs up memories of past hurts that caused you to feel unloved, arousing feelings that come under the label of "unfinished business." It is as though in the mind-computer you punched a button labeled "hurt" and out flew all the cards telling of times you felt deeply hurt.

Loss of love is your reaction to all threats. And the feeling of being unloved can lead to violence or depression. Every feeling you have is registered somehow, somewhere in your mind and body, making up your inner state of being. Your feelings dictate your choices as to how to act.

Intertwined fantasies and memories spin through your unconscious in haphazard disregard of time, for the unconscious has no sense of time; yesterday is as today. As they did for Penfield's patients, the memories stir wishes and fantasies connected to earlier losses and hurt—fantasied or threatened loss of the genitals in the phallic period, loss of feces in the anal period, loss of the mother's breast or the warmth of her body in the oral period, and perhaps the earliest loss of all, felt as you were born, loss of her breathing for you when you were in the womb.

There are other losses, less acute ones, that a child must endure, such as the loss of a relative, particularly a grandparent, the parent of his mother or father; or the death of a beloved pet. A child mourns every loss even though he represses his grief.

Fantasies from childhood are apt to be intense, as Dr. Eduardo Weiss and Dr. O. Spurgeon English point out in their book *Psychosomatic Medicine:*

> When the relationship to the mother with all its significance to the child (and carried into life in the unconscious) is threatened, or when a person is under stress, the longings for help or consolation are expressed in various combinations or forms in different persons: wanting to be fed, wanting to be carried or led; wanting to be snuggled and sheltered, and so on, reflecting the oral, ambulatory, dermal, respiratory, and other mechanisms and forms of attachment to the mother.

There is first and foremost the longing for the love of the mother, the wish to satisfy the early erotic urges. There is an unconscious attempt to regain the lost breast, then the lost feces, then the lost penis—one object from each of the psychosexual stages.

But you can never regain what has been lost in spite of your wishes, wishes that are still so strong within that if you have not made peace with them, they may find expression at times in physical illness.

A very successful businessman came to see me when his marriage was breaking up. He was feeling very depressed, as though, he said, he was "near tears all the time." He felt apathetic, weary; it was an effort for him to get dressed each morning to go to work. Tall and handsome—any woman's idea of a perfect escort—he refused to go out evenings with any of his friends.

One day as he was telling me of his depressed feelings, tears came to his eyes. I knew how difficult it was for this self-made, independent man to show tears in front of anyone—man or woman.

"Why are you crying?" I asked gently.

"I don't know," he said slowly. "It's just that I feel all alone in the world. Without a friend."

"As if you need your mother to comfort you?" I asked.

He looked alarmed. "You mean I'm a crybaby?"

"Not at all. None of us ever gets over the need for a mother's love when we feel defeated or deserted. There is a part of us that never grows up. A part that always needs a mother's love, whether we're eight or eighty, though most of us try to hide the need."

Eventually, as he was able to bring himself to accept this, his depression lifted. He regained his former vigor, went to work eagerly each morning. And he began calling women for dates. When he was ready, I thought, he would probably find a second wife.

Actually, you punish yourself for many of the wishes and fantasies of childhood, now thought evil and obscene, though they once stemmed from a need to express natural urges. You may stop up your nose so you cannot breathe the air you fantasy may make you pregnant or kill you with its poisons. Or you may lose your sense of smell and of taste, or sense of vision or hearing or ability to speak. In the various losses displayed in your body, you tell of the feeling that you have indeed lost something.

3

NECK AND THROAT

The thyroid gland, located in the neck, has been called *la glande d'émotion*. The influence of the psyche on endocrine function has been forced on the attention of physicians by even superficial clinical observation, as they grant that the pathological function of the thyroid comes about as a result of psychological distress.

Hyperthyroidism is a particularly vicious cycle, for not only is it caused by anxiety but the illness itself leads to increased irritability, which in turn heightens the feelings of dis-ease.

World War II focused the attention of physicians on the importance of psychic trauma in causing hyperthyroidism in general and in men in particular. Many cases of hyperthyroidism in soldiers after battle were reported. Studies of civilians with thyroid disorder revealed that all reported some emotional shock just before they contracted the disease.

The thyroid gland takes part in the visceral expression of emotion. Patients with thyroid conditions who go into therapy find that their thyroid condition becomes normal as they feel more at ease within themselves.

Dr. Israel Bram, discussing the psychic factor in exophthalmic goiter reviewed 3,343 cases of goiter, concluding that the history of each person usually revealed three important facts: (1) "nervousness," exophthalmic goiter, or diabetes mellitus, in at least one blood relative, (2) "nervousness," irritability, impatience, and a tendency to violent emotion in the patient usually since child-hood, (3) the beginning of the symptoms soon after a psychic trauma.

Dr. Bram concluded that 85 percent of the 3,343 cases "pre-sented a clear history of psychic trauma as the exciting cause of the disease." He said his data pointed strongly "to the irrationality of thyroidectomy in the treatment of exophthalmic goiter." He proposed instead efforts directed "toward endocrine and mental adjustment."

One of the pioneers in psychosomatic medicine in America, Dr. S. E. Jelliffe, in "The Psyche and the Vegetative Nervous System with Special Reference to Some Endocrinopathies" *(New York Medical Journal)*, describing the case history of a woman with hyperthyroidism, concluded:

> We as physicians must first straighten out her ethical conflict. Removing the thyroid does not do this, even if we admit that she has gotten her body into such a mess that she would rather die than renounce the *wish*. For this happens and only surgery may prevent the unconsciously arrived at physical suicide. What happens after-wards, even if the thyroid be removed?

The late Dr. Nolan D. C. Lewis, former director of the New York State Psychiatric Institute, in his article "Psychoanalytic Factors in Hyperthyroidism" *(Psychoanalytic Review)*, reported two cases of hyperthyroidism treated by intensive psychotherapy. In both instances the major improvement came after the analysis of conflicts about masturbation, he said, citing this as "the princi-pal factor in the conflict of forces producing the hyperthyroid stage."

Dr. Lewis commented, of thyroidectomy:

> A thorough study of the fundamentals of the personality by the psychoanalytic method attempts and more often succeeds in pulling out also the roots of the weeds, thus producing more permanent results and a more complete understanding of the mechanism in-

volved. Thyroidectomy removes a symptom in the syndrome, thus breaking the arc and often producing temporary relief or disappearance of a group of symptoms, but it frequently fails, for after all surgery is powerless to remove the underlying predisposing factor and its by-products in the personality. It is only an expression of therapeutic common sense that we insist that the psychotherapy be instituted as early as possible in the disorder in order that its possibilities may be realized before permanent damage is wrought either in the organic components of the system or in the mental sphere of the patient.

In fantasy, a goiter may symbolize a baby, displaced from the uterus to the throat (which is also a cavity through which substances pass). Even men may have this fantasy, since little boys sometimes say they want babies by their fathers, before they learn this is impossible.

A woman came to my office just after she had a goiter operation. She was fifty-five years old, and her face looked as though she had been through a lot of suffering in her life. She was married to a real estate broker, and they never had any children.

Tears came to her eyes as she told me this. She said, "The sorrow of my life has been that I have never been able to bear a child."

In fantasy, she *was* fulfilling her wish to have a baby, in symbolic form.

Thyroid disorders are characterized by a lack of iodine in the system. A study of changes in blood iodine in fifteen people under emotional stress showed that the iodine level increased over 20 percent in thirteen, over 50 percent in nine, and 100 percent in three.

Some authorities have suggested that a habitual clearing of the throat, as though to expel something irritating, if kept up over weeks, months, years, may have such a drying effect that it could eventually cause cancer of the throat. Illnesses of the throat may symbolize in some the act of fellatio in which the throat is involved as a substitute uterus. The movie *Deep Throat* held such wide appeal not only because of the subject matter but because it carried out the fantasy of fellatio.

A tall, handsome man in his fifties, an architect, came to see me, sent by his doctor. He was slow but sure in his bodily movements. He dressed immaculately and in expensive suits.

This man would feel at times that he was choking to death and would get paralysis of the glottis which only spirits of ammonia or smelling salts would relieve. His doctor could find no physical cause for the choking fits or the paralysis.

I asked him, "Do you remember thinking about anything in particular the last time you suffered such a fit?"

"Only that I felt a sense of shame and guilt," he said.

"About what?" I asked.

"I got divorced from my wife about a year ago, leaving her and our two children, and I have felt consistently ashamed and guilty. I had fallen in love with a girl twenty years younger. The age of my daughter, in fact. I moved into her apartment. It was fine at first. But then I began to feel fed up with her. At times I hated her. I even felt she was not safe with me, that I might hurt her. So I moved away. Took an apartment of my own. Got a puppy to keep me company. I see her when I feel like it. She doesn't understand, but she says she loves me and goes along with the arrangement. I feel ashamed about that, too."

He added, "I know I'm unreasonable, that the little things she did that irritated me another man could have stood. So there must be something wrong with me."

"Have you fallen in love with younger girls before?" I asked.

"Ten years ago I was unfaithful to my wife with a young secretary at the office. Sometimes I would spend the night at her apartment. It lasted six months."

"How did you end that affair?"

He looked at me with a pained expression. "I tried to commit suicide. But not very seriously. I swallowed a bottle of aspirin. It was just a gesture because I felt so guilty."

He "swallowed" the aspirin, an act that involved the throat, I thought. There was something about "throat" that meant agony in his life.

This was proved three weeks later when he came to a session with a cringing, horrified look in his eyes. I asked, "What's the matter? Don't you feel well?"

"I know I have to tell you everything, Dr. Stevens," he said, "but this won't be easy. I think it's the most difficult thing I've had to do in a long time." He stopped.

"Psychiatrists are accustomed to hearing about every kind of behavior known to man," I assured him.

He swallowed nervously several times, then, "Last night when I got home from the office I felt very depressed. I was so upset I was not aware of what I was doing. The puppy was barking piteously. I guess she wanted to be fed, or taken out for a walk. She wouldn't stop barking. Before I knew what I was doing I bent over and picked her up and — and — and my hands tightened on her throat and I strangled her."

I thought "throat" again, and this time death to a dog.

He let out a piteous cry. Tears came to his eyes. "I—I—killed a little, innocent dog," he moaned. "With these," and he held out his bare hands, hands that had tightened in fury around the puppy's neck. And he suffered from paralysis of the neck.

This man felt "choked"— that someone was "choking" off his life—and in turn he wished to choke, but instead displaced his feelings on an innocent little puppy, giving it to her "in the neck."

I knew he felt guilty about causing the dog's death, but the important thing was to help him bring to awareness feelings of violence that had driven him to this desperate deed. Such violence belonged to childhood. No reasonable adult would need to kill an innocent puppy, no matter how long the puppy barked or how irritated the adult felt.

In the next few sessions this man talked about his feelings for his mother and father. I learned that when he was seventeen, his father had choked to death from a piece of steak caught in his throat. Thus my patient's fantasies of being choked to death were an identification with his father, sort of a reunion in death, for he and his father had been extremely close, even though his father, a very strict man, sometimes whipped him for misbehaving. His father had been an architect, and my patient, who had adopted that same career, unconsciously was afraid he would also follow in his father's footsteps dying from something that would attack his throat. In one sense he was keeping himself from dying by making it impossible for him to eat whenever he felt guilty, as though he deserved to die—a feeling that followed his desertion of women. He spoke of his mother as a beautiful woman to whom he also felt close. This would mean he felt guilty about his boyhood yearnings for her, which he had obviously never outgrown.

Illness is also used as a method of punishing the self. It is a fairly direct way, since the unconscious works on the basis of an eye for an eye, the primitive law of revenge—both revenge dealt out to others and that expected by the self for crimes either committed or imagined. This man had to punish himself for his unconscious death wishes as a boy for his father—wishes he had never admitted to himself. They arose whenever his father had chastised or struck him. He had to punish himself by falling ill in the same way his father had died.

It took months before I dared interpret this to him, for a psychiatrist must gain the trust of the patient before he can make the deeper interpretations. This was a man who, because of severe emotional conflicts, had been unable to look upon a woman as a human being. It took two years before he was able to accept that the failure of his marriage had been his fault as well as his wife's. The only kind of woman he had been able to tolerate, and then not for long, was a very young woman whom he could treat virtually as a slave, but then despise, so that he would have to walk out on her, too.

As he could become more aware of his very early childhood conflicts, including a great oral need for his mother (the throat is part of the oral process because of its swallowing function), and he could accept responsibility for his deeper feelings, his throat condition cleared up. Months went by without one single complaint of paralysis.

After three years of therapy he was quite a changed man. He could accept his desire for violence as stemming from the childhood rage at being whipped and felt he could control it. He did not go back to his former wife, but became engaged to a woman only three years younger than he.

A young, attractive blond woman, who had lost the use of her vocal cords, was admitted to Saint Vincent's Hospital in Santa Fe when I was a member of the staff. I had been at a party when she was admitted, but since I was on call, I was summoned to the hospital to find out what was wrong with her. I was wearing a deep blue chiffon evening dress and a blue star sapphire ring. When I got to the hospital, I took off the dress and stepped into my white coat, but kept the ring on.

The young woman was unable to say a word. She had no concussion. I ran a series of medical tests for urine and blood to rule out a diabetic coma. Her husband and two children stood by the side of her bed looking frantic.

Her physical examination was negative from the reflexes of her eyes to the reflexes of her toes. The cause of her inability to speak must be psychological, I thought.

I decided to try to talk to her. I asked her husband and children to leave the room. Almost hypnotically, I started to assure the young woman, "You will feel better. You will feel much better. You will want to talk." I sensed somehow she was mute from panic.

It was late in the evening. One of the lights in the room was shining on my blue star sapphire ring and it sparkled, as though alive.

The young woman suddenly spoke. She exclaimed, "What a beautiful ring!"

Not letting her realize that this was a breakthrough, I said casually, "I'm glad you like it. I've had it a long time." Then I asked, "Did anything happen to you last night or today that might have affected your vocal cords?"

She nodded, then said in a whisper, "My husband and I had a terrible fight."

"You and your husband?" I was surprised because he seemed so genuinely concerned about her.

"Yes. He started to shout at me last night because dinner was late. I can't stand anyone raising his voice at me. I had been delayed because I was taking care of Susie's knee. She hurt it playing in the yard. So I started getting dinner very late."

"Did you explain this to him?"

Tears came to her eyes. "I couldn't. I can't defend myself. I just clam up. I shut my lips tight and don't say a word."

"You mean you go mute instead of fighting back when you feel put upon?"

I thought, she cannot fight, nor can she flee, so she uses a bodily defense to protect herself from harm.

"I know I'm a coward," she said. "But my father brought me up to speak only when I was spoken to. He would hit me across the mouth if I dared talk back. He was a very strict man."

When she felt angry at her husband, she had no way of expressing her feelings. Instead she would shut herself up so she would not antagonize him and risk the slap in the face her father used to give her as a child.

All it had taken was concern and interest on my part—the feeling that someone cared—to enable her to speak again. After all, at the bottom of all illness is the feeling nobody cares. Everyone who falls sick is in need of love. Often what a doctor gives that is most important is not medicine but the feeling of love, diluted, but love nonetheless. Or, at the very least, the feeling that he wishes the patient to get better and stop hurting. In many instances, this is enough to effect a temporary cure.

"In the future try to speak to your husband and tell him what you are thinking when you feel angry," I said to this young woman. "Bottled-up anger can be a boomerang. It is not fair to yourself, or him, to go mute. Look what he is going through now. He is suffering far more than if you had talked back to him."

A faint smile appeared on her face. "That's true, isn't it?"

I summoned the husband and children. I said, "She's all right now."

"She can speak?" Her husband looked at me as if I had performed a miracle.

"Yes. And if you're thoughtful and gentle with her, she'll tell you why she had to lose her ability to speak."

I changed back into my blue chiffon dinner dress intending to return to the party. On the way, I studied the sparkling star sapphire ring and thought reflectively of the part it had played in enabling a frightened young woman to regain the use of her vocal cords.

4

SHOULDERS AND ARMS

Arthritis, a disease that cripples hundreds of thousands of persons, often strikes in the shoulders. It may appear in any of the muscular joints of the body, however. Formerly referred to as rheumatism or lumbago, it is caused by a muscular spasm that produces pain that may at times be excruciating.

Changes in muscle tonus are among the most frequent mechanisms of psychic expression and are particularly amenable to therapy. They are connected to an inhibition of the desire to carry out activity involving the muscles. According to Dr. Franz Alexander, "Chronically increased muscle tension brought about by sustained aggressive impulses appear to be a pathogenic factor in rheumatoid arthritis."

As an example, Dr. G. L. Engel and Dr. A. H. Schmale report arthritis suddenly appeared in the ankle of a man who admitted he felt the strong impulse to kick down the door of a girl friend who had rejected him. He unconsciously paralyzed the joints of his ankle to prevent himself from acting on the powerful impulse, which stemmed from his desire for revenge.

In other words, inhibited hostile impulses may lead to increased muscle tension. The hostile impulses originally seek discharge through muscular contractions, but they are inhibited. Arthritics have a strong inclination toward muscular activity that they are forced to restrain. As an arthritic can express his rage, frequently his muscles will relax and the arthritic condition disappears. In arthritis a calcification of the joints takes place as though the person were continually building up his resistance to a powerful urge.

The study of the dreams of patients suffering from arthritis shows a propensity to express repressed tendencies through the use of skeletal muscles. A study conducted jointly by the Psychosomatic Institute of the Michael Reese Hospital and the Chicago Institute for Psychoanalysis reported a greater than normal degree of muscular response to emotional stimuli in arthritic patients.

In ancient days arthritis was attributed to the spell of witches and the weather. Cold, rainy weather seems to increase the pain, but then does not such weather usually increase feelings of depression?

My father, who suffered from arthritis, used to wear an old remedy, a catskin, the furry side turned inward. The warmth of the animal's skin probably helped ease the pain, since heat seems to do this. We associate heat in our unconscious with the warmth of love, and cold with the absence of love. We speak of someone as "a cool cat" when he can remain detached from the impact of his emotions.

The pain of arthritis may disappear temporarily with the use of tranquilizers and heating pads, but the psychological causes have to be uncovered psychoanalytically in order for any "cure" to be lasting. As Dr. Paul Schilder said, "It is impossible to regard activity as a sum of reflexes unless you put a psychic idea into your reflexes." Those "psychic ideas" must be brought to awareness before the arthritic pain will disappear.

I heard of a policeman on the New York City force who suffered from arthritis of the shoulder. A psychiatrist who interviewed him found out this policeman was continually holding back from shooting when he caught a criminal. He was calcifying his arm unconsciously so that he would not give in to his hostile impulse to pull the trigger on a thief.

Aggressive impulses may be closely tied to sexual ones. Rage and sexual desire are often present together, and it is difficult to separate them. But if you study the reactions of a baby, you are apt to conclude that rage follows wishes to be loved, fed, taken care of, which are infantile sexual wishes. Only when these wishes are frustrated does a baby feel rage. There is one exception— when an attack is made on his life. Then rage comes first, for all other emotions are subservient to self-preservation.

The close connection between rage and sexual desire appeared in a case I encountered while working in Santa Fe. This case had to do with an ailment of the hip, not shoulder, but the psychic mechanisms are the same.

One day about noon I received a telephone call. The voice was that of a young woman. She said, "I've got to see you right away, Dr. Stevens. It's an emergency."

"What's the trouble?" I asked.

"My right hip is paralyzed. I can hardly walk. I'm unable to go to work."

"When did this happen?"

"This morning. I hitched a ride to work. That's when it happened. I can't explain over the telephone. Will you give me an appointment?"

I was puzzled, wondering what hitching a ride could have to do with a paralyzed hip. I told her, "Of course. Come in right away."

"I can reach your office in twenty minutes. Thank you." She sounded relieved.

As she hobbled into my consultation room a short time later, I saw a very pretty girl, with fragile features and dark hair flowing to her waist. She appeared to be about nineteen years old. She crossed to a chair, favoring her right hip, and lowered herself with great difficulty into the seat. She looked at me in silence, as though it was too difficult for her to talk.

"What happened this morning?" I asked gently, wanting to help her get started.

"It happened." The wide brown eyes had a sad expression in them.

"What do you mean by 'it'?" I again felt puzzled.

"My mother told me never to allow it to happen until I got married. Now I don't know what to do." Her face was stoic, as though she would not allow herself to feel.

"Tell me the details." I realized "it" meant sexual intercourse.

She sighed, then said, "I usually walk to work every morning. I'm a secretary in Mr. Smith's law office." He was a prominent lawyer in Santa Fe. "It's about a mile from my house, and I usually don't mind the walk if the day is pleasant. I stroll along the highway and enjoy the early morning sun and fresh air.

"But today it was so hot that I felt very uncomfortable as I walked along. I thought I'd never reach the office. When I was about a quarter of a mile from it, a car stopped alongside me. A handsome young man was driving. He was blond, and he had a charming smile. He asked me, 'Don't you want a lift? You must be very warm.'

"At first I said no. I thanked him for his kindness. I was really afraid to be picked up by a stranger. Not that anything had ever happened to anyone I know. But my mother and father have always warned me against hitching a ride in a car."

Tears came to her eyes and she looked ashamed. I waited for her to go on, giving her a sympathetic look.

"The young man said, 'I'm harmless. I work in town at the local car rental agency. I've seen you walking to work many a morning but never dared stop. I didn't want you to think I was fresh. But it's really very hot today. Please let me give you a lift.'

"He sounded so sincere, so friendly, that I finally said 'Okay.' He opened the door and I got in. We exchanged small talk for a few minutes. After a moment we approached the railroad crossing where you turn left to go to the office where I work. I said, 'Please let me off here. I can walk the half block to the office.'

"But instead of stopping, he speeded up the car. He turned right, into that old dirt road that leads up into the hills. I said in surprise, 'Where are you going?'

"He said, 'It's early. I thought you might like to see a view of the city from a new spot I found. It's breathtaking.'

"I was frightened to death, but I didn't want him to know it. I thought, someone this handsome and friendly can't possibly want to do anything wicked. So I tried to make a joke of it. I said, 'We should have brought coffee and rolls and had a second breakfast.'

"He drove up and down some steep hills, then parked the car in a small clearing, out of the sight of everything. It was surrounded by bushes and trees. I wasn't even frightened then, believing he was a gentleman. But then—"

Her eyes again filled with tears. She continued, "He leaned over and forced me down on the front seat of the car. He started to get on top of me. I tried to push him off. I said, 'Please don't! You seem so nice. I don't understand.'

"He said, 'I won't hurt you. You'll like it. It'll make you feel good.'

"I started to cry. I said, 'I've never done this before. You must believe me.'

"He wouldn't listen. He was very strong, and he hitched up my skirt and pulled down my pants. Before I knew it, he was inside me. Then he did it."

"In the front seat of the car?" I was surprised. She must have been extremely uncomfortable.

"Yes. He pushed my right leg up and out of the window. It hurt. Oh, how it hurt," and she broke into sobs.

"Let me examine your hip," I said.

I asked her to perform certain movements, to make sure the hip had not been injured. I could find nothing wrong.

I realized the hurt was in large part psychological. This had been rape, but a rape that she had, in a way, invited, first by allowing herself to be picked up by the handsome young man, then by not insisting he let her out when they neared her office. Part of her had wanted him to make advances, it seemed clear— that part that was now punishing herself by paralyzing the right hip, the one that had been thrust through the window to make possible the act of sex.

"Do you want to press charges against this man?" I asked, knowing that her bottled-up rage against his sexual aggressiveness was part of the reason for the paralyzed hip. She was suffering not only because of her guilt, but because of the rage at her seducer which she was repressing.

"No!" Her tone was horrified. "The publicity would be worse than anything I could possibly suffer."

"Even having a baby?"

"Even that." She sounded determined.

"Can you tell your mother about this?" I thought her mother might understand and give love and solace.

"I don't dare! She'd never forgive me. And she'd tell my father. And he would probably kill me."

Even though I found nothing wrong with her hip, I sent her to the hospital for X rays. They showed no damage to her hip.

She returned to find out the results of the X rays. I was certain this was a case of hysteria conversion, where the organ afflicted served as a symbolic substitute for the tabooed sexual one. Since I was not then a psychiatrist, I suggested she make an appointment with a psychiatrist in Santa Fe, which she agreed to do. I asked her to call me after she had seen him and let me know the results. I said to her, as she left my office, "Please tell him everything that happened. He has to know, in order to help you."

"I will," she promised, holding out her hand. "I'll do whatever you say."

She called me two weeks later, said she had visited the psychiatrist five times and would continue seeing him. She reported that her hip was now normal. She also said her regular menstrual period had taken place, and she felt very relieved.

Then, in a lower voice, as though very embarrassed, she told me, "The young man has left town. I guess he was so ashamed he couldn't bear facing me."

I realized that she considered this reasonable enough punishment for his crime, one in which she had unconsciously participated. I wondered, though she had not discussed it, to what extent she had flirted with the young man and led him on. This would have had to occur in view of the punishment she had inflicted on herself via the arthritic right hip.

Another instance comes to mind, one quite different, but showing how arthritis may sometimes be relieved if a person feels wanted, if a lowered self-esteem is raised.

I was looking for a housekeeper in 1959 for my home in the country which has nineteen rooms and five baths. I advertised in the local newspaper. A woman called up and said she was bringing her godchild over to meet me and hoped she might get the job. We arranged a time.

At the appointed hour, a car stopped in front of the house, and out of it walked an attractive young woman followed by a crippled old lady. She walked painfully into the house. She told me she had arthritis of the arms and legs so badly she could hardly move at times.

The three of us talked, and I agreed to give the younger woman the job as housekeeper. But she could not start for two weeks. Whereupon the crippled old lady, who looked about seventy, said, "If you'll have me, I'll substitute for her for the two weeks."

I looked at her in surprise. She said, "I have worked most of my life, until this arthritis hit me. I once owned a nightclub in New York."

"Well, I don't know—" I was dubious, wondering how she would manage to move around.

"Let me try," she begged.

I sensed something in her that was pleading desperately, as though for her life. I said suddenly, "All right."

She lived in her own home nearby and told me she would drive to work each day. I hoped she would make it. The first day she appeared, she struggled once again to get out of the car, then limped stiffly into the house. She had to walk up and down stairs, as part of her work, and I could see the tears flowing down her cheeks because of the pain as she hobbled up and down. It ended up that I waited on her because I could not stand her agony. But she insisted on staying the full day and doing as best she could under the circumstances. I decided I could put up with it for two weeks if she could.

Day by day she seemed to get stronger. At the end of the two weeks, she walked up and down the stairs without any pain. She said to me, "I don't want to leave you. Will you accept me as housekeeper instead of my godchild? She doesn't care."

First, I sent her to her regular physician, wanting to make sure that her condition had cleared up enough so she could stand the pressure of the job. The physician told her, "You should keep working. There is an unbelievable change in you."

Gradually I learned more about her background. Her husband was dead, she was English, and had come to this country as a little girl. When her nightclub became a success, she started buying property in New York, later in Connecticut, where she now had her own home.

I decided to try her for a while. Fourteen years have gone by, and she is still my housekeeper. Today, in her early eighties, she does not walk—she "runs" up and down those stairs. She has no arthritis. She seems ageless.

This is a woman who does not need money but needs to keep busy. She gives what she earns to poor relatives and senior citizens in the community who are in need.

Several years ago she decided that being my housekeeper, and doing the cooking and cleaning, did not keep her busy enough. So she bought a delicatessen in the neighborhood. She cooks the soups and makes the salads for this delicatessen, getting up at five in the morning to do so. She loves her work so much that when I told her to take a vacation, she felt hurt.

One might say, in a sense, that this woman is able to productively use muscular energy heretofore dammed up which had caused her arthritis. An active woman all her life, when her husband died she had felt so depressed that she had retreated from all outside interests, mourning far beyond the usual one year. She had found it difficult to return to any kind of vocation or

avocation. But her attitude had changed, had become more positive, when the position at my house became available. She suddenly had decided she wanted it so much that she would risk the
pain of her arthritis in order to get and keep the job. The work
proved so beneficial to her, psychically, a sign that she was coming
out of her depression, that her physical pain also vanished. Would
that all arthritic sufferers could find this happy an easing of their
suffering.

What, according to the psychoanalysts who did the original
research on impeded functioning by the muscles, is the cause of
heightened (hypertonus or dystonic) or excessively lowered
(hypotonus) muscle tension that impedes or inhibits or weakens
the muscles and results in arthritis, sacroiliac, or bursitis?

Psychically speaking, Dr. Otto Fenichel, a pioneer in the study
of psychosomatic illness, says these conditions are "determined by
the action of instinctual defenses, especially the repressive activity
of the ego." Our ego refuses to carry out an impulse to act and,
in order to avoid a conflict with our id, compromises by partially
gratifying the impulse.

In the paper "Organ Libidinization Accompanying the Defense against Drives," published in 1928 in the *International
Journal of Psychoanalysis,* Fenichel discusses the causes of muscle
spasms throughout the body (including in the stomach and excremental organs), or what he calls "greater or smaller dysfunctions
of the musculature."

In describing "the repressive activity of the ego," he explains
that repression consists in keeping given impulses from motor
expression, or action. Such impulses include ones we believe dangerous to our survival or self-esteem, such as the impulse to kill,
to have indiscriminate sex, to commit rape, or to steal. Excluding
such impulses from consciousness is our way of achieving this
denial of the wish to act.

In other words, our ego renounces certain movements. It is this
inhibition of motor expression that the ego "is at pains to apply

to the substitute formations of the repressed instinctual impulses as well, so that even they are debarred from being translated into action," says Fenichel. "From the inhibiting of motor expression of substitute formations there may in general develop a *partial limitation of the ego's command of motor expression,*" he adds.

Thus the actual purpose of repression is to prevent the carrying out of an instinctual impulse. The ego of a child is continually forced to suppress motor impulses of an autoerotic, erotic, or aggressive nature. He must not steal another child's toys, or he must not "play" with his own genitals or those of other children. In certain instances, the motor inhibitions thus established are maintained throughout life.

Psychoanalysts have reported about some patients in analysis that when they appear to be resisting an interpretation about some particular behavior, all the muscles in their body seem to stiffen. It is as if the patient were trying to resist the emerging awareness of the repression by means of renewed muscular force.

Fenichel described a woman who at first could not speak at all in her analysis. She would visibly contract her body and clench her fists. Later, she described this condition as a feeling of "emptiness of thought." She felt her inability to speak in a bodily way —her inside was cramped, her chest and limbs so tense that they "did not let anything come out." After an hour of silence on the couch, she felt exhausted as if she had been indulging in intense physical exertion. When she could eventually talk with greater ease, it was like a sudden release of muscular tension. She would say, "I can't tell you how physical it all is."

It is not unusual during an analysis to find muscular tensions vanishing as psychic conflicts are brought out into the open. The very verbalization of an internal conflict has an easing effect on the body; it is felt physically. Our thinking, in early childhood, is very much influenced by the functions of our body, by the demands made on our body by our instincts, both sexual and aggressive. Our thoughts constitute the way in which our intellect interprets the world within as well as without. In both a psychic and a physical sense we relate to everything that happens with either pleasure or pain, and we use our fantasy, our imagination, to try to explain through thought the cause of the pain and thus lessen it.

Fenichel calls thinking "experimental action." He says that any inhibition of thought must show itself in changes in our motility and muscle tonus just as inhibition of action does. Thus, the suspension of certain muscular abilities corresponds to quite analogous psychic inhibitions, to the suspension of certain "qualities of experience," says Fenichel.

Dr. Felix Deutsch, also a pioneer in psychosomatic studies, maintained that *"every* change in tonus, every movement and every rhythmic activity in the organism, as well as every increase and interruption of these, is an expression and effect of the current of instinctual impulses."

In other words, the way a psychic conflict is expressed in a bodily illness depends on your early experiences of childhood, your fantasies about those experiences, the kinds of illnesses you suffered as a child, the way your mother reacted to these illnesses, and the illnesses your parents had that you may have adopted through identification with them. All this adds up to the specific bodily defense unconsciously used by you to repress an instinctual impulse you feel is dangerous to give in to.

That the sexual drive is the one often repressed may be seen in the fact that the most extreme cramps people can suffer take place in the muscles of the pelvis, both its floor and the joints of the hips.

Our first ego is a body ego, as Freud said, and the threat of damage to the body is the most primitive and basic of all threats. The customary reaction is one of tremendous anger. We may also react to a psychological threat as though it were a threat to our body. I told one woman, who would not accept the slightest criticism from anyone, "You are reacting to a suggestion as though it were a blow to your body." This is often a natural feeling.

Not only anxiety, but suppressed rage, may be expressed in the body as muscular spasms. Scientists have shown that suppression of the motor discharge of any emotion leads to an increase of muscular tension.

I recall the instance of a former boxer who, when he had to retire from the prize ring, started to suffer from acute muscular pains in his neck. The aggression he had formerly been able to release by hitting his opponents now had to be repressed. But the wish to release aggression was seen in the muscular spasms in his neck, a most vulnerable spot for a boxer.

Muscular spasms may also indicate sexual fears and wishes. Rhythmical and continuous muscle spasms, as well as all kinds of muscle play, such as tics, may symbolize masturbation in the unconscious. Psychiatrists have long noted that the spasms in hysterical neuroses may signify distorted sexual gratifications.

As we pointed out earlier, every repression requires a continuous spending of psychic energy. Our ego cannot, or cannot always, manage to make headway against an undesirable impulse by withdrawing the psychic energy from it. It also must erect a barrier, which means extra energy must be used to block the impulse. This is costly to our psychic processes.

The wish to act and the wish not to act struggle against each other within our muscles. The muscle spasms are an expression of the struggle between contradictory impulses which, keeping each other in balance, "fixate" a quantity of what Freud called "organ libido" in the place where the struggle is going on.

Sandor Ferenczi assumed that a trauma, the solution of which was unsuccessful, left a depot of stimuli in an ego memory system or somatic memory system. He believed that under certain conditions the stimuli that issued from these depots, which acted like drives, attained direct outflow into motility. But more frequently, such an outflow fails to come about, prevented by the ego, and the libido remains dammed up in the somatic memory system. Ferenczi gives as example: "These are the neurotics who become conspicuous by the excessive caution, measuredness, and weightiness of their manner of walking and movements"—those whose function of motility is impeded.

Actually, almost any traumatic experience can result in the buildup of a kind of residue of stimuli or basic drives in the fantasy of our minds so that any attempt to prevent expression or liberation of these drives creates a blockage in our muscle network, affecting motion and movement.

Our bodily sensations become conscious as a sensation arises from the depths of our body and is then relayed to the brain, where we become aware of it and can consciously act on it. On the way, however, a sensation may be hampered or impeded by the intervention of the unconscious part of our conscience, as it acts automatically to protect us. Such a sensation may be called, in Freud's words, "an unconscious sensation."

These unconscious sensations can be conceived of as a discharge reaction that succeeds in overwhelming our ego before a sensation can occur. Or as a discharge reaction that does not take place at all. The ego thus successfully shuts itself off from forbidden internal perceptions, just as it does under certain circumstances against external perceptions.

In other words, we may be furious at someone for insulting us but not even be aware of our fury if we feel our rage so dangerous that if we become conscious of it, we believe we will kill that person. Or someone may put his masturbatory impulses into his work, pounding a typewriter or painting a picture, and wonder why he gets little satisfaction out of what he does, not aware that he is frustrating a deep sexual impulse.

Just as the ego defends itself against ideas that, as derivatives of repressed instinctual representations, seek their way to consciousness, so does it defend itself to a certain extent against corresponding internal perceptions. For instance, a woman may have no feelings in her genitals during intercourse as a defense against giving way to sexual feelings she believes will drive her out of her mind with their intensity.

All too often the very organs that have a particularly high erotic quality are the ones in which it is hardest to obtain feeling. But if an individual can face his hidden sexual and hostile fears, he will experience new sensations in his body and also possess a new sense of identity and peace within. This is what takes place in psychoanalysis.

5

THE HEART

High blood pressure, which plays a significant role as the underlying cause in the more than 1,500,000 heart attacks and strokes Americans suffer each year, affects persons in all walks of life—farmers, businessmen, housewives, athletes, and the underweight as well as the overweight. The disease may lurk quietly in the body for years, then suddenly attack.

It is the largest single cause of all deaths in this country. About 24,000,000 Americans suffer from high blood pressure (about one in seven), and half of them are not aware of it. Less than one fifth of those who have it are under adequate treatment, according to physicians. It is the primary cause of about 60,000 deaths each year.

The influence of emotions on the heart has been carefully studied by both physicians and psychiatrists. Dr. S. I. Schwab called emotion "the most common heart accelerator." Studies show that even while sleeping, the heart rate of nervous persons is not as reduced as in the less tense.

Hypertension and arteriosclerosis, with vascular spasms occurring in these conditions, are, beyond question, caused by emotion. Any condition resulting from vascular spasm may be considered psychogenic. Even the contraction of a small coronary vessel just for a few minutes may lead to localized anemia and weakening of the vessel wall, and when the contracted vessel again opens,

69

hemorrhage may result. From a number of small hemorrhages, chronic inflammatory processes develop. Spasms of psychic origin in small coronary vessels may cause numerous lesions of the myocardium. One physician reported the case of an aviator who said he had experienced attacks of tachycardia over a long period of time, then recalled they occurred each time he made a parachute jump. Tachycardia is palpitation of the heart, an acceleration of the heartbeat due to fear.

In a frightened animal the blood vessels will constrict and spill adrenaline, from the adrenal glands, into the circulatory system. This has an accelerating effect on the heart (part of the fight or flight reaction noted by Cannon). You can understand what happens to the heart if someone lives in a constant state of fear from real or imaginary dangers. Fear thus will take its toll by creating physical disturbances of the cardiovascular system as the pulse rate is increased.

Studies have been made both of reflex responses to momentary sensory excitation from the outside world and "ideas" aroused by inner stimuli. Investigators found that "ideas" from within increased the pulse and blood pressure more than sensory stimuli from the outside. That is, the anxiety within us that emanates from our fantasies does more damage to the heart than our response to a threat from the outside world.

Dr. Paul Dudley White, authority on heart ailments, states in his book *Heart Disease:*

> Even allowing for missed diagnoses in the past, angina pectoris has evidently increased in frequency, and is encountered more in communities where the strain of life is great and a hurried existence the habit than in leisurely parts of the world. . . . The situation is appalling and demands some action on our part. Almost certainly the most effective move that we can make is to call a halt on the world's mad rush of today.

In 1782 a physician reported only three women out of one hundred suffered from angina. Dr. White gives the ratio today as one in three. He advances, as a possible explanation, the fact that women have entered into the competition and strain of business and professional life.

Of all psychosomatic studies, those relating to blood pressure and blood distribution are among the earliest and the most extensive. Among the most important findings of early studies was the inverse blood distribution in limbs and body surface on the one hand, and in the viscera (the internal organs of the body, such as the intestines, heart, and lungs) on the other. That is, with pleasurable emotions there ensues an increased blood flow to limbs and body surface and a decreased blood flow to the viscera, and vice versa with unpleasurable emotions.

Scientists found that the mere "idea" of an intended motion caused an increased blood flow to the respective limb. But this increase did not take place on passive movement of the limb (that is, if someone else moved it) if at the same time the idea of motion was not present. Numerous experiments also showed that an increase in blood pressure with muscular work is due essentially to psychic factors. The increase remains about the same whether the muscular work be considerable or slight, provided the psychic effort is the same. Blood pressure increases of from 178 to 210 mm on the mere hypnotic suggestion of muscular work, though none was carried out, were observed in some studies. People under the influence of hallucinations or delusions also showed an increase in their blood pressure.

Other studies showed a rise in blood pressure when persons were shown pornographic pictures, when asked to decapitate a live rat with a butcher knife, or when a firecracker exploded near them.

There have been instances when remarks about high blood pressure were made by physicians to patients, which resulted in a serious hypochondriacal preoccupation with the blood pressure on the part of the patient, leading to chronic invalidism, the giving up of a job, and retreating to bed. These were cases in which the blood pressure may have increased at the moment of a single reading under emotional stress, though otherwise it was probably normal, or at least not high enough to interfere with the patient's normal activities.

That a traumatic event may cause a heart attack was illustrated recently when an American cargo vessel, *The Sea Witch*, outbound in the early morning darkness of June 2, 1973, ploughed into an oil-laden Belgian tanker lying at anchor just off Staten Island north of the Verrazano-Narrows Bridge in New York Harbor. The crash touched off an inferno of explosions and fire. The fifty-five-year-old captain of *The Sea Witch*, John Paterson, of Clifton, New Jersey, died not of burns or drowning, but of a heart attack suffered on the deck of his ship at the time of the crash. The shock had been too great for his heart.

Anthropologists have reported that healthy, vigorous young men and women living in primitive tribes who believed they had broken a tribal taboo have died within a few days of a heart condition. Cases are also reported where patients in healthy condition died on the operating table even before the anesthetic was administered. Doctors suggest that there may be a fear of suffocation, resulting in an angiospastic increase of peripheral vascular resistance against which the heart may fail.

The expression "to lose heart" indicates psychically what may happen physically if someone gives up, wishes to die. He stops his heart from beating. I have known of such cases.

A woman in her sixties who was very depressed lay down one morning on the couch in her daughter's home and announced, "I'm going to die," and promptly did. Her autopsy showed no pathology, no physical cause of death. She had simply stopped her breathing by the fervent wish to die. Her daughter was planning to remarry which meant she had to move out of her daughter's house and live alone. This no doubt made her feel unwanted and forced to face the torment of living alone, a torment she could not tolerate.

When I was practicing in Santa Fe, a man of forty-eight came to my office one day and announced, "I'm going to die. An inner voice keeps telling me my time is up. I have money, all

I want, but I have nobody to care whether I spend it or save it. Nobody in the whole world loves me."

He had been examined by the finest internists in town who found nothing physically wrong. But within this man, a life-and-death struggle they could not measure was being waged. He was certain he was going to die. He said to me wistfully, "I'd like to die in bed."

He seemed in such a state of panic that I took him across the street to the emergency room at Saint Vincent's Hospital and asked the Mother Superior to give him a bed. He was placed in a private room, and a doctor was summoned to examine him. As the doctor was going over him, the man died. An autopsy was performed, and it showed there had been nothing physically wrong with him.

Here was a man who felt alone, unwanted, with no love in his life. He wanted to die, and did. Thus do some die of heart attacks without any obvious warning, when there is a strong wish to die at a particular moment, a wish to give up life's struggles.

This is a kind of suicide, since suicide is the destruction of one's body. Suicide is rage turned inward. This rage is transmitted over different pathways of the body, first going through the lymphic system in the brain. Rage turned inward, rage at the frustration of erotic or aggressive desires, is transferred to different parts of the body by the nervous system which supplies the body organs with their motility.

One might say it is rage at the frustration of an erotic or aggressive wish that causes a person to overeat. Because the wish is unconscious, the person cannot fight the devastating hunger he feels that causes him to consume excessive calories. He may have the wish, from childhood, to be pregnant by a tabooed sexual mate (the parent of the same or opposite sex) or to devour hated siblings of childhood or a parent who frustrated him. It is difficult for him, without help from a psychiatrist or psychoanalyst, to face such thoughts, though they are perfectly natural to a child. Instead he keeps overeating and may bring on a heart attack, rather than face the deeper conflicts of the heart.

While overweight is a definite factor in the cause of heart failure, it is not always the cause. An outstanding internist I knew was as thin as the proverbial rail. He told me he ate very little because he wanted to remain thin and save his heart.

"I have a feeling I'm going to die young," he said. "That's why I'm so careful of my diet. I don't want to die of heart failure."

He was a man who drove himself day and night, in his office and at the hospital. He was always fatigued, always tense.

One day he died suddenly, at the age of forty-four—from a heart attack. Tension had taken its toll of his heart in spite of his thin body.

Compulsive eating often stops as a result of therapy. I had a patient with an obsessive craving for chocolate éclairs. She was a young, intelligent high school teacher. I can only compare her craving with someone addicted to drugs or alcohol.

She was forty pounds overweight but could not keep herself from devouring a dozen or more éclairs every day. She had tried many diets and was able to eliminate all fattening foods but the coveted pastries.

She lived with her mother, and on her way home from teaching school, she would stop off at a special store and buy a dozen frozen éclairs. Sometimes she would reach home with an empty box, having eaten all of them on her way, and would have to turn back and buy more as dessert for the evening meal. She never got sick from éclairs—she could eat as many as she wished.

She told me that at times she would go on a crash diet and lose ten to twenty pounds when she went out of town and there were no stores that sold frozen or fresh chocolate éclairs. She had several sets of wardrobes—she would wear the clothes that fitted her at certain weights as the scale went up and down.

She decided to get psychological help and came to me for two years, three times a week. She was a very tall girl so that she could carry weight, but not the weight she had put on from the chocolate éclairs. Her blood pressure had risen, and the doctor had told her to lose weight if she did not want to endanger her life with heart trouble.

As she talked on the couch, it became clear she thought her life "empty" and had to stuff "sweets" into her system to make up for the sweetness that was lacking in her life-style. Her father had died when she was seven. She had a younger brother, who was her mother's favorite. She recalled her mother stuffing her with "sweets" when she was little to pacify her.

We talked about the symbolism of the chocolate éclair, as we discussed why she chose that particular kind of sweet in which to indulge herself. She confessed she had always envied her brother and wished she had been born a boy. (The shape of the éclair is like a phallus, and there is also the filling, the white cream, symbolic of semen, covered by dark chocolate, symbolizing the hair out of which the penis grows. On the earlier oral level, the white cream symbolizes milk, the éclair itself, the breast. On the anal level, the comparison is obvious, in both shape and color.)

The need for sweets also represented an overwhelming need to comfort herself as she mourned the death of a father she never knew well, feeling deprived of his love and protection.

At the end of two years of treatment, she had lost forty pounds, she was able to go weeks without one chocolate éclair, and she had fallen in love with the history teacher at her school whom she planned to marry. Her blood pressure had returned to normal.

Overweight is caused by anxiety. So often you hear the story of the typical high-pressured executive in his late forties or early fifties whose family lives in the suburbs, who commutes daily to his office in the city, and who drops dead of a heart attack on the golf course or running for a train.

One such man came to me because he was fifty pounds overweight and could not stop eating. A routine physical checkup that his company had provided showed that his cholesterol count was very high. He was ordered by the doctor to go on a diet and lose fifty pounds.

He was unaware of the strain under which he lived. He spoke

of his sixty-mile-a-day train rides to and from his home as "joy rides." In addition to work, he led a social life that took up all of his leisure time. He would go daily for business luncheons, drinking cocktails and eating rich foods, then imbibe more cocktails and rich foods that night in the suburbs. Late at night he would throw himself exhausted into bed to rest for the next day and the same routine.

In spite of my advising him to go slowly, he went on a crash diet and lost forty pounds in two months. Then he died. The crash diet had been too much for his system. When you diet quickly, your body suffers. Weight should be taken off slowly. The cholesterol has to be broken down gradually.

I believe that, in a diet, both proteins and carbohydrates are necessary. We learned in medical school that "proteins can burn adequately only in the fire of carbohydrates," the fire being the metabolism of the body. If you eat two eggs, which are protein, you should also eat a cracker or a piece of bread to furnish carbohydrates. Otherwise your kidneys may rebel.

One proof that tension causes high blood pressure is seen in the decrease of tension in old people, whose blood pressure goes down as they become slightly senile and openly display selfishness and self-centeredness, feeling the world now owes them a living and others can take care of them.

Then there is hypoglycemia, or low blood sugar, which is very much in the news these days. Cannon and others found that cats bound in a comfortable holder, if excited thus even for so brief a time as half an hour, developed glycosuria, an excess of sugar. They concluded, "The fright or rage of the animal is the essential element." The promptness with which the glycosuria developed was directly related to the emotional state of the animal. Sugar was found at an early stage in animals that showed immediate signs of fear or rage. Sugar appeared much later in those animals that took the experience more calmly. Three cats, which remained particularly calm, showed no glycosuria when bound in the holder for periods of up to four hours. But when an energetic little dog barked at them, they became excited and sugar showed in their urine.

Cannon examined the urine of twenty-five members of a Harvard football squad right after the final and most challenging contest of the season. He found sugar present in twelve members. Five of these were substitutes never called on to enter the game. An excited spectator whose urine was examined also had marked glycosuria.

Other scientists studied medical students after they had taken a difficult examination and found glycosuria, though normally all had no sugar in their urine. Hypoglycemia was found in aviators, varying in amount according to the degree the aviators experienced fear. Neurotic soldiers, as well as normal soldiers, showed glycosuria for two to three days after being exposed to fire.

Studies dealing with the influence of hypnosis and suggestion on blood sugar levels showed that hypnosis per se did not influence the blood sugar. That is, it was not possible to prevent an increase in blood sugar after the intake of one hundred grams of glucose by giving the suggestion under hypnosis that this was only water. Or to produce an increase in blood sugar by the suggestion to the person that he was taking sugar when he was given water. But it was possible to eliminate most of the hypoglycemic effect of an adrenaline injection by the suggestion that the injected substance was only water.

Dr. R. T. Woodyatt, who wrote a classic textbook on diabetes, said he believed the degree of diabetes varies in response to nervous and emotional influences. He cited the case of a businessman, sixty-five years of age, who was in a hospital on a diet where he was given a small dose of insulin for his diabetic condition, and was passing normal urine. Suddenly, with no change in regime, his urine showed increasing amounts of sugar. A careful physical check revealed no cause. Then it was learned he had just heard his corporation was taking steps to retire him.

Dr. Woodyatt comments, "It is interesting to be able to measure the power of emotion in terms so tangible as ounces of sugar.

The power of emotions to produce physical alterations of the body does not seem unreal under these conditions."

An interesting experiment was conducted by Dr. Fritz Mohr in 1925. He reported the case of a man with glycosuria whom he hypnotized. He told this man under hypnosis that his intense emotional reactions toward certain people in his environment who disturbed him would be eased. After the hypnotic session, the man was sugar-free. Then Dr. Mohr told him, under hypnosis, he would be upset by these people. When the man came out of the hypnotic trance, his urine held 2.5 percent sugar. This experiment was repeated four times, always with the same result.

Some physicians observe that people who give "the impression of nervousness" are more inclined to develop diabetes than calmer people. They stated that "this disturbance of function may be brought about by way of pathologically altered nervous impulses."

The symptoms of hyperglycemia include anxiety, irritability, excitement, confusion, and, in the extreme, complete loss of consciousness. Some people behave during such an attack as if they were drunk or slightly mad.

Euries Ferré in 1897, appears to have been the first to study directly the influence of emotional excitement on the blood count. He found in students who had just completed an examination an average of 457,000 more erythrocytes per cubic millimeter of blood than before the examination. The higher blood counts corresponded to the most excited, and the lowest to the most "indifferent and phlegmatic" members of the group.

Many studies in animals have shown that their blood count increases dramatically if something frightens or enrages them. Emotional excitement of ten to fifteen minutes duration in a group of cats causes an average increase of 13 percent in mononuclear cells, returning to normal in twenty to thirty minutes.

If we apply these findings in specific emergencies to a person who feels as though he were undergoing a psychic emergency almost every minute of the day, we can see how the steadily reacting systems of the body would become overtaxed and eventually break down. It is not natural for a person to act as though there were an emergency all the time, living in a constant state of fear and rage.

If someone does not face his psychic conflicts but keeps calling on his body to react constantly as though in a crisis state, chances are he will fall physically ill. Psychic conflicts are caused by the imagination. A stimulating fantasy can increase your heartbeat. Frightening thoughts can affect your pulse rate.

The thoughts that do damage are unconscious. They have a more destructive effect on the body than your conscious thoughts, according to Freud. For your conscious thoughts can be controlled. But you have no control over unconscious thoughts. They keep pounding away at your body, demanding incessant release. However, if you can become aware of them, the dammed-up psychic energy in these thoughts no longer has to be vented on the body, but is freed for conscious acceptance.

This permits a more positive mental attitude in confronting life's many and varying problem situations and, at the same time, will help you to maintain a greater degree of physical and mental well-being.

6

THE CHEST

It is through our breathing, whether calm and easy or agonized and difficult, that we tell in part how we are coping with life's vicissitudes. According to legend, when God created man, He breathed into his nostrils the breath of life, and thus man became a living being.

Life begins and ends with a breath. Dr. G. R. Heyer, who studied the process of respiration, concluded that the inhalation of oxygen and the exhalation of carbon dioxide could be regarded as one of the most deep-lying and fundamental of vital functions.

The taking of one breath is a very complicated process, though most of us do it easily and automatically. Not only the nose is involved but passages in the head, the throat, the lungs, the shoulder girdle, the spinal column, the muscles of the thorax, and the diaphragm. All these parts of our body participate and, in turn, are influenced in their development by the way we breathe.

There is also an interaction of our respiratory apparatus with the abdomen and its walls and contents. In addition, breathing affects our posture, and vice versa. What we think of as the "bearing" of a person, both physically and psychologically, has much to do with the way he breathes. We say, "There is an air about him."

The use of the Homeric word for "diaphragm" as the seat of the emotions shows that the ancients connected the emotions with breathing. The influence of emotions on our breathing seems evident even to the layman who can observe his own difficulty in breathing when someone annoys him or frightens him and is aware of the rapid breathing that accompanies the sexual act.

Physicians have discovered that one result of prolonged heavy breathing may be a lack of calcium in the blood, with increased alkalinity. Breathing may also affect the action of the heart and the endocrine system. In fact, there is probably no part of the body our breathing may not affect if it goes awry.

After a series of experiments in which a number of persons were subjected to forced breathing, which resulted in extreme carbon dioxide output and a state of excitement and nervousness, the persons then experienced a period of lassitude and depression. This condition, as well as the previous excitement, was "reminiscent of frustrated sexual excitement," stated Dr. Heyer. He noted that the cardiac and diaphragmatic discomfort especially were "suggestive of phrenocardia: pains and anxiety states from which individuals sexually excited and frustrated often suffer."

He pointed to the unique significance of respiration for the human organism, in that respiration, though an automatically governed function, can also be consciously controlled.

Asthma is a prevalent respiratory illness that has been studied intensively by psychoanalysts. They discovered that asthmatic children show an unusually strong attachment to a mother from whom they cannot, or dare not, separate. The wheezing of the asthmatic has been compared to a "cry for the mother." The child feels such a deep identification with his mother, almost as though he were one with her, breathing along with her, that he cannot accept any separation from her without deep protest.

A young man who could hardly breathe because he suffered such severe attacks of asthma went to Dr. Eduardo Weiss for help when Dr. Weiss, a psychoanalyst, was practicing in Trieste in the early 1920s. He wrote an article about the young man with asthma which was "a pioneering contribution to psychosomatic medicine," as Dr. George H. Pollock, director of the Chicago Institute, said in an obituary for the *Psychoanalytic Quarterly* when Dr. Weiss died in 1970. The article, never translated into English, was titled "Psychoanalyse eines Falles von nervosem Asthma [Psychoanalysis of a case of nervous asthma]."

The young man's asthma attacks had developed in childhood as reactions to fear of separation from his mother, Dr. Weiss concluded, after helping him overcome the disease. The attacks represented, said Dr. Weiss, a sort of "strangulated cry" to regain the mother whose love he felt he was losing.

Dr. Weiss compared the sight of an asthma attack to "the shrieking, helplessly sprawling newborn child with blood-red, swollen face." In the case of the young man, the fear of his mother's disapproval and rejection had been intensified because she had been very intolerant of any show of sexual interest on his part when he was a boy and he had to repress all sexual curiosity and outlets.

Twelve years later, in the article "Bodily Pain and Mental Pain," Dr. Weiss described how the feeling of loss of a mother's love was accompanied by deep grief:

> When we lose someone we love, quantities of libido within the ego are torn away from the ideas of the real object and there ensues mental pain which sets going the process of grief. This process, the work of mourning, is comparable to the healing of a wound. Love-objects become, as we know, libidinally bound to the ego, as if they were parts of it. If they are torn away from it, the ego reacts as though it has sustained mutilation. The open wound thus produced in it is just what comes to expression as mental pain.

The mental pain, in many, becomes converted into asthma, their unconscious choice of physical suffering.

According to the Allergy Foundation of America, at least 9 million persons in this country have asthma. It is the leading cause of limitation of activity among children under seventeen, and every year 5,000 persons die because of complications that develop from it. About 134,000 persons are hospitalized every year because of asthma, for an average stay of eight or nine days. One quarter of these are children.

In World War II 37,000 persons were discharged from the armed forces because of asthma, though they had all passed the recruitment medical examination and presumably had been in good health at the time of induction.

The word "asthma" is derived from the Greek *aēnai*, which means to breathe hard. The severity of the disease can range from mild and occasional attacks to episodes so acute that hospitalization becomes essential. The sufferer experiences difficulty in breathing, wheezes and chokes, and sometimes seems to be suffocating. The bronchial mucous membranes become irritated and inflamed, and the inflammation obstructs the passage of air through the bronchial tubes and causes phlegm, which creates further obstruction. The controlling bronchial behavior muscles become subject to spasms, and these also block the passage of air. Over the years, if asthma is not properly treated, the lungs may lose their elasticity and the chest eventually become distended and barrel-shaped, leading to the chronic condition known as emphysema.

At all ages, stress or excitement may provoke an attack; even a prolonged bout of laughing or crying can bring an attack on. Asthmatics may be sensitive to external factors such as extremes of weather, pollens, dust, pets, and certain foods.

Dr. Margaret W. Gerard, a Chicago psychoanalyst who, with several other psychoanalysts, studied the psychic causes of asthma, wrote of their findings in an article, "Bronchial Asthma in Children." She cited a previous study, by Dr. C. H. Rogerson and others, of twenty-three asthmatic children, in all of whom was found great anxiety and lack of self-confidence. During the psychological examinations, the children became very anxious when left alone with the examiner. The younger ones refused to be separated from their mothers. All preferred not to answer questions rather than risk making a mistake. In a play group the asthmatic children were quieter and seemed more repressed than the healthy children. A few of the older ones made frequent exits from the room to make sure their mothers were outside.

The parents of these children were found to be protective "to a pathological degree" in seventeen out of the twenty-three cases. In some instances the excessive protective attitude was due to an attempt to overcome guilt feelings resulting from a deep hidden hostility to the child.

In treating the children, the psychoanalysts attempted:

> . . . to change the over-solicitous behavior of the parents into a more affectionate but more permissive attitude in order to allow the child a greater degree of independence. At the same time, the child was encouraged to enter more independent activities to facilitate a decrease in the anxiety which he experienced when away from the mother. In a significant number of the cases treated, the number and severity of asthmatic attacks were noticeably decreased.

The evidence seemed to indicate that the asthma attacks were definitely connected to a fear of separation from the mother.

One little boy of seven was brought to me by his mother because of asthma attacks. Her family physician called in advance to say, "This is a mother who won't let her son out of her sight. She's stifling him and doesn't know it. His asthma would let up if she'd let up."

The minute the mother and son walked in, I knew what the family physician meant. She clung to her son's hand, and he to hers, as if they felt that any temporary separation would be an irreparable loss.

"Please sit down," I said, indicating one chair for her and one for the boy.

They let go each other's hand reluctantly. The little boy looked as though he were going to cry. He started to wheeze. He was, I realized, very frightened at being in a psychiatrist's office.

It is very difficult to help an overprotective mother relinquish her unconscious hold on a child. In this case, obviously the mother had to be helped to become aware of why she clung to the little boy, and her son had to be helped to dare to become more independent.

I suggested that the boy be sent to a child psychoanalyst while the mother kept a regular schedule of appointments with me for a while. She agreed, and for the next few months she came to my office three times a week and spoke of her feelings. They were chiefly about her own mother who, in like fashion, had overprotected her. As she realized she had been treating her son in precisely the same manner as her mother had treated her, and could verbalize her great dependence on her mother and understand how crippled and dependent she had always felt, she was able to give her son greater freedom. In turn, he was helped by the child analyst he was seeing to become more assertive, and his asthmatic attacks vanished.

The asthmatic stifles his urge to cry out, but the cry emerges nonetheless in the form of the wheeze and difficulty in breathing during an attack. The asthma victim feels it is too dangerous to cry out because he fears he is losing his mother. A child who has been ridiculed for being a baby because he clings too closely to his mother may develop a wheeze instead of crying out in pain. This compensatory action is partially a plea, partially an enraged stoppage of the respiratory system.

One psychotherapist reported that almost three quarters of the asthma sufferers who came to him for treatment had undergone nose or pharynx operations, yet there had been no change in the asthmatic condition. But the asthma cleared up as they relieved emotional tension by becoming aware of unconscious conflicts.

Beneath the "strangulated cry" of the asthmatic lies another feeling, in addition to the fear of separation, according to Dr. Felix Deutsch. There is also a "latent hatred" of the mother that conflicts with the need to cling to her.

The feelings of love and hate do not exist separately but are very close in childhood. A child may love a mother one minute as she feeds him and hate her the next for leaving him alone.

It may be difficult for an adult to be aware of what Freud called ambivalence—mixed feelings of love and hate. As a child, when you felt angry at your mother as she frustrated you, you hated her and had an impulse to destroy her, since hatred—the natural reaction to frustration—carries with it the unconscious wish that the hated one drop dead. But this impulse came into conflict with an opposite impulse—to preserve her—because she was the only one in the world who would love you and take care of you.

There is a mutual interaction between our body's emotional and physical processes whether they proceed normally or abnormally. This interaction, once it has been expressed in physical illness, may remain inactive most of the time except under stress. The interaction may form a psychosomatic complex that has the potential to react as a unit, and in a specific way, whenever one part of the unit is stimulated.

For instance, as a child you may have received special sympathy whenever you coughed. As an adult in a situation in which you feel you need sympathy, you may cough in an unconscious attempt to get sympathy.

A woman walked into my office one morning, and the first thing she did was to suffer a fit of coughing. She was thirty-nine years old, tall and well dressed, a highly successful executive in an advertising firm, and had just married.

She told me this in a series of staccato sentences punctuated by coughs that put a deep flush of color in her cheeks. I asked sympathetically, "Do you have a cigarette cough?"

"I don't smoke," she said.

"Have you had the cough long?"

"All my life," she replied. "It comes and goes."

"Do you notice that it appears at certain times?"

She said in embarrassment, "Yes, particularly when I'm nervous. I guess I'm nervous now." She coughed again, trying to stifle the spasm by placing her hand to her mouth. This woman coughed as another person might nervously clasp and unclasp his hands, or sigh, or cry.

"Is anything particular on your mind at this time?" I inquired.

The immediate response was a series of coughs. Then, slowly and reluctantly, came the confession: "I just can't handle them."

"Who?" I asked.

"My husband's two children by his former wife. They live with us. His wife is an alcoholic, and the court awarded the children to him. They're little monsters." There was anger in her voice. She paused, then continued as though confessing a heinous crime, "I hate them! I wish they'd go live with their mother. My life would be so easy without them." No cough.

As she talked on about her feelings, I noticed the coughing stopped. At the end of the session she said, "I feel much better telling you my troubles. May I come back?"

"Of course," I assured her.

She had been sent by a friend of hers, another patient of mine who suffered from depression. The woman with the cough remained in therapy for several months, during which time she continued to ventilate her feelings about the children. Simultaneously, she dredged up out of the past her own experiences with her mother who had been a very difficult woman to live with and constantly imposed her personality on her daughter. At the end of four months she was able to live more harmoniously with the two children. She had even started to like them and to become an adequate substitute mother. Her cough had completely disappeared. It had been, in a sense, a bid for sympathy every time she felt she could not cope with a difficult experience in her life.

Dr. Deutsch said that in normal circumstances we breathe according to the oxygen requirements of our bodies, but under emotional stress the involuntary movements of the breathing musculature involved in respiration overreact in compulsive fashion. Something interferes with the automatic regulation. The interference is not conscious but represents a compromise between an emotional need and the normal automatic bodily responses that are unconscious. He cited studies of breathless women that showed them to be very submissive, expressed in their shallow breathing.

Certain emotional conflicts tend to afflict certain internal organs and processes, according to studies made at the Chicago Institute for Psychoanalysis. For instance, inhibited rage seemed to have a specific relationship to the cardiovascular system. Dependent self-seeking tendencies appeared to have a specific relationship to the functions of eating and digestion. A conflict between sexual wishes and dependent tendencies seemed to have a specific influence on the respiratory functions.

The psychological component in bronchial asthma represented a retreat from action into a dependent, helpless attitude. Because of the close correlation between emotional tensions and the respiratory functions, it was stated by the institute in reports that in most diseases of the respiratory functions psychological factors probably played an important role. The asthmatic symptoms were exaggerated and chronic responses to underlying emotions. The exaggerated and chronic nature of the response was basically due to the fact that the emotional stimulus was unconscious because it was unacceptable to the conscious.

One woman of thirty-two, a very attractive dark-haired woman, could hardly get out a word that did not sound as though it were delivered as her last breath. Every sentence was uttered in a breathless, little girl manner.

She was engaged to be married but had delayed setting a date for the wedding. She was a research assistant on the staff of a large weekly magazine where her fiancé was an editor.

She bit her lips as she said breathlessly, "I really don't know why I keep putting off the wedding."

"Perhaps you don't want to get married," I suggested.

"Oh, it's not that!" She looked as though I had suggested she were planning a murder, not a marriage. Then she added in explanation, "I guess I'm afraid of losing my identity."

I thought to myself, "You really feel you have no sense of identity, because people with a strong sense of identity do not fear to lose it."

I asked, "Tell me something about your parents."

"I adore my father, though I'm scared to death of him," she admitted. "My mother is frightened of him, too. She has submitted to his iron will all her life."

"And are you afraid you will have to submit to the iron will of your fiancé?" I asked.

She remained silent for a moment, then said, in a voice that, for a change, was not breathless, "I think you've hit the nail on the head. I'm afraid he'll be another Papa."

"He doesn't have to be—unless you make him so in your mind," I said.

"How can I prevent that?"

"By looking at the relationship between you and your father, and your father and your mother," I said.

It took time, but session after session, she talked about her feelings after her father would bawl her out when she was a little girl and she would not know what to say or think or do. "Once in a while, I would dare to try to speak for myself, but the words came out in a breathless way," she admitted.

That breathless quality had continued to be part of her reactions whenever she felt frightened. As she realized her fear stemmed from childhood experiences and that there was no longer need for it, the problem disappeared.

Studies of asthmatics conducted at the institute showed that the basic psychodynamic factor in asthma was a conflict that centered in an excessive, unresolved dependence on the mother.

As a defense against this infantile fixation, all kinds of personality traits may develop. Persons suffering from asthma may be aggressive, ambitious, argumentative, daredevilish, and also hypersensitive, aesthetic types. Some asthmatics are compulsive characters, whereas others have a distinctly hysterical nature. Common to all is a repressed dependence on the mother, a characteristic around which different types of character defenses may develop.

The dependence seems to have a different connotation from

that found in those who suffer from gastric neuroses and peptic ulcers. Its focus is not so much the oral wish to be fed but the wish to be protected. In contrast to the ulcer cases, fantasies of eating and feeding are not exaggerated. Instead, there is a high frequency of intrauterine fantasies which appear in the form of water symbolism or entering caves or other closed places. Everything that threatens to separate the person from the protective mother is apt to precipitate an asthma attack. The birth of a brother or sister, an act that threatens to absorb the mother's attention, is found with frequency at the start of the condition of asthma, as though the illness were a protest against the newcomer.

In adults, sexual temptation or impending marriage may be a precipitating factor. For the young girl, the acceptance of the biological function of womanhood is the turning point as she separates from her mother, becoming her mother's competitor instead of the dependent child.

For the son, incestuous wishes threaten his dependent relationship to the mother. Studies show that most mothers of asthmatic boys and men are very sensitive to signs of their son's physical attraction and react with withdrawal or rejection, out of their own sexual fears.

An asthmatic condition may start when a son is contemplating marriage. He may have a conflict between his dependent attachment to his mother and his love for his fiancée. He is likely to have had a mother who at times acted unconsciously seductive to him and at other times rejected him.

One young man of twenty-three with an asthmatic condition came to see me because he was having difficulty setting a marriage date. He was tall and thin, wore glasses, and had a prepossessing friendly manner. He seemed to wheeze only when he felt intensely about something he said. He told me, "My fiancée, Mary, sets a date and I agree, and then when I confront my mother, she has a million excuses why that date is wrong, and I can't defy her." He wheezed.

"You speak of 'confronting' your mother, as though she were an enemy," I observed.

"I guess I feel that way." He did not wheeze.

"Are you afraid of her?" I asked.

He sighed. "I guess I am and I never realized it." Still no wheeze.

"It will take time for you to overcome your fears, for they were instilled at an early age," I said. "But why don't you make the first step and set a date and keep to it, no matter what she says or thinks."

"I will." He sounded determined.

He saw me for several more sessions, during which he spoke of his fear of talking back to his mother because he thought he might hurt her. I tried to help him see his exaggerated dependence on her and her unconscious willingness to take advantage of his good nature. Eventually, he did get married, and his mother attended the wedding, though she cried excessively. Of extreme importance to me was that when last I saw this man, his asthma had vanished.

Rage against the one who is loved may also threaten the dependent relationship and provoke an asthmatic attack. In the life of an adult, any experience that threatens his independent functioning may revive the deep-seated conflict between his independent and dependent tendencies and precipitate an asthma attack.

How does a repressed desire for the mother produce a spasm of the bronchioles, the physiological basis of the asthma attack? Psychoanalysts believe it is somehow connected to crying. Most asthma patients report it is difficult, if not impossible, for them to cry. Psychoanalysts have also observed that when an asthmatic patient can cry, the asthma clears up.

There has also been improvement in the asthmatic condition in a number of instances after the patient confessed an act about which he felt guilty and expected to be rejected. The very process by which the individual tells about what he considers to be reprehensible behavior tends to confirm or buttress the dependence or reliance upon the psychiatrist which was disturbed by the guilt feelings of the patient. The act of full communication precipitated in the confession enables the patient to regain the esteem and love of the person on whom he is now depending.

Confession to an adult can be likened to crying by a child. Deliberate suppression of crying often leads to respiratory problems. Evidence of this fact can be found in watching a youngster who attempts to keep from crying, or giving in to the urge, then tries after a long period to stop the crying spasm. The violent wheezing that occurs strongly resembles an asthma attack.

Allergies are popularly supposed to cause asthma. But then you have to ask why a particular person is subject to an allergy when others are not. He must have some need within that causes him to be supersensitive to ragweed or spices or chocolate.

The fear of being alone (in the unconscious, away from the mother) was noted in many a patient. One man always got an attack when he closed the door at night and put out the lights. Another related that all he had to do was open the door of his house and look out over the vast fields in front of the house to get an attack. A cigar vendor regularly developed attacks after coming in contact with tobacco.

The classic paper on the psychological interpretation of asthma and other respiratory illnesses was written in 1931 by Dr. Otto Fenichel, called "Respiratory Introjection." The concept of respiratory introjection was first described by Freud in 1918 in his case study "From the History of an Infantile Neurosis." The was the story of the Wolf Man, as he became known, because his dream of several white wolves sitting motionless in a tree led Freud to important insights about the effect on a baby of seeing or hearing a mother and father in the act of sex.

The Wolf Man was possessed by phobias, including one that affected his breathing. Whenever he saw beggars, cripples, or very old men on the street, he felt compelled to exhale forcibly "so as not to become like them," and under certain conditions (Freud does not specify what these were) he "had to draw in his breath vigorously." This meant, said Freud, he was unconsciously inhaling, then exhaling, the image of the beggar, cripple, or old man. Freud related this to the heavy breathing the man had heard from his father during sexual intercourse when, as an infant, he had slept in his parents' bedroom.

Fenichel was the first to write in detail of the importance of respiratory introjection, the childhood fantasy that you "take in" through your nose the image of someone as a means of keeping him close. Freud called this "incorporation of the lost object." In fantasying the incorporation of what he believes the lost mother, a baby consoles himself by thinking, "My loved object is not gone, for now I carry it within myself and can never lose it." These are the words of Dr. Karl Abraham, psychoanalyst, who studied the early psychic stages of the infant and how it affected later behavior. The "loved object" is the image of the mother as she feeds him, either by breast or by bottle.

Elaborating on Freud's theory, Fenichel emphasized the erotic qualities of respiratory introjection. He maintained that the mother of infancy is seen by the baby as giving both protection and "satisfaction in the erotic aspects of feeding." This "protective sexual satisfaction is unconsciously perceived as the aim of respiratory introjection," he said. In other words, breathing in the image of the mother is sensed by a baby primarily as an erotic act.

Primitive people, psychotics, and children believe they can breathe in substances from the outer world and return substances to it. The substance "is invisible and therefore suitable for conveying magical ideas, which is reflected in the equation of life and soul with breathing, which further lends itself to magical use because it is the one vegetative function that can be regulated and influenced voluntarily," Fenichel said.

You may regulate your breathing to imitate someone else's rhythm, thus trying to become one with him. Inhaling the same air as another person carries the implication of being united with him, whereas exhaling means separation.

Breathing in the image of someone loved is not only the first incorporation and an entity in itself, but it then becomes part of the oral process as the nose is used for smelling food. There is a close relationship between oral needs and breathing and smelling, intimately involved as they are in swallowing, chewing, vomiting, and food mistakenly going down the "wrong pipe," Fenichel points out. Recent studies show that sucking, swallowing, and breathing in infants form a single reflex mechanism, which makes the emotional connection a close one.

The idea of incorporating an object by breathing it in or smelling it is the expression of a particular sexualization of the respiratory and olfactory function, according to Fenichel. Psychoanalysis has shown, he said, that whenever breathing is sexualized, quantities of anal and oral libido are displaced to the function of breathing, just as happens in the sexualization of the function of thinking.

"But breathing is more primitive than thinking, and it is to be assumed that there is an autonomous respiratory erotism, which, though not intense in itself, gains importance through the displacement of quantities of oral and anal energy onto it," Fenichel says.

Freud coined the word "libido" to represent the erotic energy present from the time of birth, perhaps even inside the womb. A baby first expresses his libidinal urge in the wish to be cuddled at his mother's breast or warmed by her body. Then he discovers the pleasure of urinating and defecating, and his erotic energy becomes invested in these functions. When a little boy discovers his penis and the pleasure he gets out of touching it, and the little girl her clitoris, libido becomes diverted to the genital organs.

The libidinal drive goes through four main stages of what Freud called psychosexuality—oral, anal, phallic, and genital. In the oral stage the mouth is the focus of pleasure. In the anal stage the excretory process becomes the focus of both the erotic and the aggressive drive for both sexes. In the phallic stage, for boys and girls, the phallus becomes the organ of worship (girls wish they had a penis and envy boys the extra pleasurable appendage).

In the genital stage one supposedly becomes mature enough, physically and psychically, to love a member of the opposite sex both sensually and tenderly.

If the libidinal impulse were left to itself, possibly all would be well with the organs of the human body. But the attempt to become civilized decrees otherwise. And thus throughout life there is hatred and there is sexual desire that must be repressed.

The process of respiratory introjection is a normal, natural one. It produces physical illness only in those instances where definitely neurotic manifestations appear due to sexualization of the breathing process. Such neurotic manifestations may be asthma attacks and exaggerated breathing habits of certain people suffering from obsessions.

Someone who has asthma may be displaying a regression caused by sexual attachment to his mother which appears in converted form as the symptom of asthma. The asthmatic has transferred his conflict between himself and his mother to a conflict between himself and his breathing process.

A fear of breathing, expressed as anxiety, may also result from a dread of suffocating that a baby may have experienced shortly after birth or in the first few months of life. A fear of castration from the later phallic stage may also be expressed in the feeling of anxiety expressed by abnormal breathing.

Our breathing processes are at the very root of anxiety. A baby's breathing is an important part of the experience of birth and thus of the anxiety that may be present during the rest of life that may stir memories of this first frightening situation. The connection between anxiety and breathing is so close that psychoanalysts have speculated as to whether special sexualization of the breathing process is not frequently caused by the sexualization of anxiety.

That is, the intimate linkage between anxiety and breathing may mean that fluctuations of breathing, such as those involved in asthma, are based upon the existence of an unconscious preparedness for anxiety situations. Sometimes during analysis patients will stop their breath momentarily or have spasms of the diaphragm when they become anxious. We could call the inner interference of regular breathing a sign that the person is mobilizing his strength to find out whether he needs to be frightened at that moment.

The wheezing and the gasping and rhythmic noises of the asthmatic may be connected to the primal scene, the hyperventilation that occurs during intercourse. It may relate also to aggression.

I remember a young woman in her late twenties who came to me suffering from asthma. She had been plagued by such attacks ever since the age of eight. Antiallergic medications did not seem to help her.

She was tall and angular and awkward in her movements, and her features were slightly pinched. There was a younger and prettier sister in the family, and my patient told me that she had always been very jealous of her sister, believing her mother and father loved the younger girl more.

During one of her consultations with me and amid wheezes and the catching of her breath, she recalled an evening when she was eight and her younger sister was six.

"We were having a pillow fight on our beds—we slept in the same room in twin beds," she said. "We often did this. Suddenly Mary put her pillow over my mouth and pressed hard, as if she were trying to smother me. At first I laughed, thinking it was a game. Then I couldn't catch my breath. I felt I was suffocating. I couldn't even get breath enough to scream. I thought I was going to die. But somehow I managed to pull free. I tore myself away from the pillow. I wanted to kill Mary. To suffocate *her* as she was trying to do me. But all I could do was stare at her in horror. And later, when my mother came in to kiss us good night, I didn't even tell her what Mary had done."

She turned to me and asked piteously, "Wasn't that an awful thing for a sister to do?"

"It certainly was," I agreed. "You must have been filled with fury."

"I guess so," she said. "Since I felt like killing her."

"Mary tried to suffocate you when you were eight, and that's the very age you started to get asthma attacks," I said. "Do you see a connection?"

"Like I was suffocating myself to death?" she asked.

"Like you were doing to yourself what you wanted to do to her. An eye for an eye, in revenge, an idea about which you felt very guilty," I said. "You didn't even tell your mother what she had done. You suffered in silence. But your desire to get even was a deep one. Not only because you felt she had tried to kill you but, as you have said before, because you thought your parents loved her more."

She started to cry. She cried on and off at her sessions for the next few months as she talked about her deeper feelings about her younger sister and her mother and father, exorcising her hatred and envy of her sister and mother. Not surprisingly, her asthma slowly disappeared. She found she could breathe normally.

Other illnesses of the respiratory system are amenable to treatment in the same way. We might say in general that illnesses affecting the respiratory system show, among other things, an unconscious wish to "breathe in" something believed taboo and then "breathe it out" with a vengeance, as it were.

7

THE ABDOMEN

As early as 1884, physicians were describing what they called nervous dyspepsia as being caused by emotional stress. They also spoke of "intestinal melancholia."

One doctor commented, "That people develop gastric disturbances after financial losses and suffer from them until their financial conditions turn to the better is an everyday experience." He estimated that between 60 and 70 percent of all patients who consulted him for gastric disturbances suffered from "nervousness."

Dr. G. R. Heyer, sensing psychosomatic implications, said, "Psychically, as physically, something may be fit to eat, to our taste, enticing, *ein gefundeness fressen* or a hard nut, we choke over many things, swallow them down or bite them off."

The stomach may react to almost every emotion and sensation we are capable of experiencing. An emotional disturbance affecting the alimentary canal is capable of starting a vicious circle. The stagnant food, unprotected by abundant juices, naturally undergoes bacterial fermentation, resulting in the formation of gases and decomposition products that irritate. These, in turn, may produce mild inflammation or be absorbed as substances that disturb the metabolism and thus affect a person's mental state.

Dr. George S. Stevenson, noted psychiatrist, reporting on a study in 1930 of 150 patients in a gastroenterological clinic, noted, "Neglect of the patient's motive and emotional problems is today lending aid and comfort to the cultist and wasting a powerful instrument of treatment."

Actually, the stomach is one of the most significant bodily organs we humans possess. It is extremely sensitive to the rise and fall of emotional tides and can be influenced by all manner of experiences and sensations that are part and parcel of individual life-styles.

There is the familiar "sinking feeling" in the pit of the stomach or cramps that may follow on receiving bad news. Experiments have shown that psychic stimuli may increase gastric secretion and that acidity in the stomach also increases as a result of un-pleasurable emotional sensations. The inhibition of gastric secretion may occur with feelings of depression. The liver is affected by emotions as well as by excessive alcoholism which, as we know, is caused by psychic conflicts.

Dr. Franz Alexander described the case of a patient suffering from a gastric neurosis connected with chronic hyperacidity. Whenever this man saw a moving picture in which the hero fought enemies or took part in aggressive, dangerous acts, he reacted with acute heartburn. In fantasy he identified with the hero, but this identification aroused anxiety and he unconsciously retreated from his aggressive feelings by an attempt to seek security and help, according to Dr. Alexander. He explained that dependent desires for security and help are intimately connected with the wish to be fed and may produce increased activity of the stomach.

"This patient behaved paradoxically insofar as his vegetative responses go, because just when he had to fight, his stomach began to overfunction and prepare itself for the intake of food," he said. "Even in animal life, the enemy must first be defeated before it can be devoured."

All forms of nervous indigestion, dysentery precipitated by nervousness, worry, or tension, various forms of colitis, and certain types of constipation, can be outward manifestations of the way our gastrointestinal system responds to emotional stress. They represent a regression of bodily responses to emotional tensions, in that they are a throwback to the patterns of infancy. One of the first emotional tensions we experience as a baby is hunger. This is relieved by taking something into our mouth which leads to the feeling of satiation. This early way of resolving a painful tension may be revived in adults at times of acute emotional stress.

A very serious man of fifty-two years with gray hair and an impeccable manner, looking as though he were impervious to all the world's problems, walked into my office one morning after having called for an appointment. He set his black leather brief-case meticulously on the floor beside the chair in which he sat.

"My doctor sent me here because I have what he calls nervous indigestion," he told me. "My stomach gets upset all the time, the moment I eat, but he can't find any physical reason why. He put me through all the routine tests. They proved I'm fit as a fiddle—as far as my body is concerned. He thinks maybe I can use some psychiatric help."

He did not sound scornful, merely resigned, as though he would try *anything*, even psychiatric treatment, to get rid of the stomach pains.

"Do you feel under pressure at your work?" I asked. He had told me over the telephone that he was a broker on Wall Street.

He laughed. "Did you ever know anyone on Wall Street who was *not* under pressure?"

"There are a number of men who take the market in stride," I said, knowing some personally. "To them it is a profession. Just like writing a book. Or being a doctor."

He looked at me, for the first time, with interest. "You mean I don't *have* to feel tense all the time?"

"Certainly not," I said. "That tenseness comes from inner pressures, not outer pressures."

Over the next few months he started to become aware of some of those inner pressures that had caused his stomach to react every time he took food into it. He had been unhappily married for ten years but decided to stick it out because of three children. Both he and his wife had mutually agreed they no longer loved each other but they would not divorce until the children were grown. He put all his libido, so to speak, into his work, and she put hers into housework and raising the children.

His parents had been rather severe with him as a boy, punishing him when he did not get good marks in school by withholding meals. Many was the night, he recalled, when he was sent to bed without supper for misbehaving or not getting a high enough mark in school. He did excel in mathematics, though, which was why he decided to become a broker.

I pointed out to him that in a way he was depriving himself of meals when he starved himself so his stomach would not hurt. This happened when he felt guilty, which he did every time he became angry at himself or his wife and the lack of love in their household. As he began to understand the cause-and-effect manifestations of those events, he was able to face his rage at the current situation, as well as his boyhood rage at his parents for punishing him unjustly. This gradual sense of enlightenment was accompanied by the disappearance of his nervous indigestion. He also discovered, after a year of therapy, that he really wanted to make a success of the marriage and that, as he grudgingly admitted, he probably loved his wife as much as he could love any woman.

A classic study as to the cause of ulcers was conducted by Dr. Alexander at the Chicago Institute for Psychoanalysis which pioneered in psychosomatic research. The study, reported in his book *Psychosomatic Medicine*, was part of a systematic investigation at the institute into the influence of psychic factors on hypertension, colitis, coronary disease, asthma, migraine headaches, and the duodenal peptic ulcer.

The gastrointestinal system was used as the starting point, Dr. Alexander said, for one reason:

The alimentary tract is a system which the psychic apparatus uses with great predilection to relieve different emotional tensions. The connection between psychic stimuli and physiologic experience is here direct and relatively uncomplicated.

Our whole concept regarding the psychogenic factors in peptic ulcers is based on the analytically well-established fact that the wish to be taken care of and to be helped, which we have so constantly found in the investigated cases, is emotionally connected in the unconscious with the wish to be fed.

What was learned about the physical cause of the duodenal ulcer is vital in understanding not only the psychic causes of that illness but others. It was discovered that the stomach of the peptic ulcer sufferer behaves when it is empty as it does when food is in it ready to digest. The stomach reacts continuously as though exposed to physiologic stimuli to which, under normal conditions, it is exposed only periodically as it contains (or is about to receive) food. The stomach shows excessive digestive movements and excessive secretion. The symptoms of nervous stomach, gastric distress, heartburn, and belching are signs of the chronic stimulation that leads to the formation of ulcers. The empty stomach of the ulcer victim acts as if it were forever demanding food and as though food were in it.

This overstimulation occurs, Dr. Alexander pointed out, not as the result of a process of nutrition but in reaction to the psychic stimulus of "longing to be loved" and "to receive or take in aggressively what is not given freely." It is as though the stomach were trying to make up for the loss of love, a love associated in the same manner as a baby does with feeding.

The emotional connection between eating and love, which we first learn as a child, remains in our unconscious as an adult. Though the majority of those who suffer from ulcers do not display the passive, dependent attitude of a child, but appear aggressive and ambitious, they are still haunted by the patterns of infantile feeding.

Studies of patients with gastric neuroses and duodenal ulcers show without exception a common feature—the wish to reassume the dependent position of the infant completely taken care of by parents.

Not only the stomach but appendix, gallbladder, liver, kidneys, spleen, smaller colon, and lower bowel may be damaged from the overactivity or underactivity that is a result of emotional stress connected with a desire to be fed—not out of hunger but out of psychic need. Eating becomes a substitute gratification for frustrated emotional needs that have basically nothing to do with natural hunger. An intense craving for love, to be cared for, followed by aggressive tendencies to devour, or to possess, form the unconscious basis of a morbidly exaggerated appetite, or a morbidly minimal appetite, which signifies that the person denies his wish to devour.

In other words, the child's world consists of his feeding processes, and his strongest emotions of pleasure and gratification become associated with various aspects of these functions. Many of his early patterns of reacting are connected with nutrition, such as the secretion of saliva and gastric juice on exposure to the sight and smell of food.

Intense rage or fear has an inhibitory influence on the functions of the alimentary tract, upon the secretion of the stomach and bowels and on peristalsis. How we feel—whether happy or sad— influences our digestive processes. The satisfaction of our hunger is closely tied to a feeling of well-being which, in turn, is connected to the feeling of being loved. To the child, to be fed is equal to being loved.

Also to the child, possession is equivalent to oral, or bodily, incorporation. He imagines that by swallowing his mother, taking her inside him, he can possess her forever and keep her from leaving him. The thwarting of this possessive tendency and of the wish to take in may lead to aggressive impulses on his part—that is, to take by force that which is not given, to bite it off, chew it, and swallow it. This is what psychoanalysts call oral aggression, and it is the cause of our first guilt feelings.

Whenever emotions of possessiveness, greed, jealousy, envy, and the striving for security become repressed, they create tension and may affect the individual via vegetative pathways to the different processes of the digestive system.

"The pleasurable physical sensations connected with the early forms of nutrition [sucking] explain the frequency of emotional disturbances of the nutritional functions, when the mature genital functions are inhibited by conflicts," says Dr. Alexander. "These repressed sexual cravings are expressed regressively in the nutritional process, and their repudiation manifests itself in eating disturbances."

A woman of fifty, who had never married, and who weighed almost two hundred pounds, came to me in despair because, she said, her stomach was always upset. She overate and feasted on the wrong foods—she lived on ice cream and cake. She worked as a buyer in a large city department store.

"It seems I walk around with a perpetual stomachache," she told me.

She complained, session after session, how depressed she felt because she had never married. She admitted, "I think one reason I never married is because I'm scared to death of sex. I was brought up in a convent where I was taught that sex is sacred. Why, I've even been afraid to kiss a man. Or 'neck' or 'pet' with him, as we used to say when I was a girl."

Here was a woman who expressed her repressed sexual cravings by overeating, which resulted in stomach upsets. She was telling of a desperate need to substitute food for sexual release which, as a normal human being, she had every right to enjoy. But she had been too frightened of her sexual feelings, as she said, even to kiss a man.

As she was able, during the months of therapy that followed, to release her fears and anger at parents who got divorced when she was a child and sent her away to a convent, she found she was able to abandon her habit of overeating, and as a result, her stomach pains vanished. Although she did not become emotionally involved with a man during the time she was in therapy, at least she started going to parties and meeting men, which was more than she had dared to do before she came to me for help.

The connection of the digestive system to the feeling of love is aptly expressed in the familiar saying that the way to a man's heart is through his stomach. Those who like bland foods, who want to avoid chewing, are showing a regression to infancy. A man of forty came to me as a patient, saying he ate only soft foods such as mashed potatoes and hamburgers—food that was easy to swallow and did not need much chewing. He would never touch a steak or celery, for instance. He had a gallbladder condition that was serious. His doctor sent him to me, suspecting he had deep emotional problems as well.

This man, a chemist, had never married. He lived with a mother who would still scrub his back at night when he took a bath, as she did when he was a little boy. Both mother and son seemed unaware that such concern on her part was abnormal. She obviously wanted to keep him her "baby," even though he was forty years old and should have been bringing up a family of his own. She did not want any other woman to possess him.

Part of this man had accepted the morbid closeness to his mother, but part of him was rebelling—the aggressive, masculine part that clamored for full sexual fulfillment with an appropriate woman. He could not express his rage at his mother, so in a sense his "bile" went into his body, into his gallbladder, which he was overusing. While in therapy he suffered such a severe attack that he had to have his gallbladder removed. Then he returned to therapy.

Over the months I encouraged him to speak about his hidden anger at his mother. Gradually he became able to express it. He started to realize he had compensated for his "lack of gall" symbolically through his gallbladder attacks.

After two years of therapy he moved away from his mother and took an apartment of his own. Subsequently, he met a thirty-year-old woman at a cocktail party and began to date her. One day he told me, "We hope to get married."

"What does your mother say?" I asked.

He laughed nervously. "I think she's resigned to it. Anyhow, I'm planning on it, no matter what she thinks."

"Good for you," I thought. "You are finally able to cut the Gordian knot, not an easy thing for a man of forty to do."

Another of my patients was a woman who had ulcers. She was thirty-nine years old and worked as an educator. She was very masculine in appearance—athletic, tall, and walked with a long stride. But she seemed paradoxically very quiet, almost shy.

She told me, "I have always felt stepped on, as though I were underfoot, that nobody wanted me around."

"How many brothers or sisters do you have?" I asked.

"I have an older sister and a younger sister," she said. "I'm in the middle."

She had been sent to me by a physician who was treating her ulcers with medication. He believed they were caused by emotional conflicts and wanted her to receive psychiatric help. He told me, when he called, that she worked very hard to keep an important job in a man's world—that of assistant administrator of a large educational institution—but that he felt socially she was an outcast.

She told me she once had been engaged, then broke it off because she didn't think she really loved the man, or that he loved her. She said with a shrug, "Who could possibly love me?"

That was the way she had felt growing up, caught between two sisters whom she believed more beautiful and more desirable. She told me her mother had wanted her to be a boy and had raised her with a boyish flair.

"Mother would dress me in shirts and pants, but my sisters always wore dresses," she said. "Both she and my father would say to me wistfully, 'You were supposed to be a boy.' "

"So you felt that to earn their love you had to be a boy," I said. "And you have tried to live like one." Then I added, "You even got ulcers, like men do."

"That's so," she responded in surprise. "I never thought of that."

Her two sisters were married, and each had a child. She said to me one day, "I wish I had a family of my own."

"We're finding out why you've been unable to do so," I said.

After a year of therapy her X rays revealed that the ulcers had cleared up. She was going out with a history professor at the university, a divorced man who seemed interested in her. She said to me quite confidently during one session, "I may even marry him one of these days."

She stopped therapy after a year and a half, and several months later I received an invitation to her wedding.

I have been consulted by high-level officials, active in government and politics, who have had recurrent attacks of colitis, diverticular diseases, and intestinal complaints. I believe there are many people under particular pressure from within and without, because of a harassing political carreer, who often have to delay their toilet functions and, as a result, may develop some physical malfunctioning of the upper or lower intestines. I have treated a number of cases in conjunction with an attending internist or surgeon, when operations are necessary, to try to relieve psychological stresses that may have caused the illness.

One statemen suffered occasional bouts of colitis. Each time he would be sent to a hospital for surgery. He was one of the most operated-upon persons I have known. I was called to the hospital either before or after an intestinal obstruction had been removed. He preferred the operations to embarking on a journey into his inner self which might have cleared up the colitis and prevented future operations.

During the few times I saw him, it became clear his personal life was very agonizing. Because of his driving ambition for political success, he had neglected his wife and three children. He would feel guilty no matter what he did—when he spent time at home he felt guilty because he was neglecting his "important" career, and while at work, he felt guilty because he was ignoring his family.

Bodily pain tells us that something is in conflict within our minds. Sometimes, when the bodily damage is so severe that there is no way to repair it psychically, operations are necessary. But operations may also be prevented if the person can come to grips with his inner conflicts.

8

THE EXCRETORY ORGANS

Food is taken into the body so that we may survive, and waste is eliminated for a similar purpose. Our excremental functions play a very important role in our emotional life.

In every infant his excremental functions become associated with the feelings of possessiveness, pride in accomplishment, the tendency to give, and the tendency to retain. Certain types of hostile impulses, such as attacking or soiling, are also associated with the eliminative functions.

The process of defecation offers the first occasion on which a child must decide between a narcissistic attitude and an attitude of loving someone else. He either parts obediently with his feces or retains them as a means of asserting his will and getting an erotic gratification in his sphincter muscles from the withholding.

We first lose the feeling that our body is our own, to do with as we wish, during the period of toilet training. It is then we learn to move our bowels at regular intervals in a specific place. This means we have to give in to someone else's demands. In return, we receive praise, love, and sometimes rewards, such as candy. Excrement becomes associated with the concept of possession and with money. Each act of elimination is considered by the child as a gift to his mother, an attitude enhanced by her deep interest in whether or not he defecates at the proper time.

This first attitude—that excretions are a gift, something valuable that is parted with, or can be exchanged for love and praise —then changes into the opposite feelings of disgust and shame. The excrement becomes an attacking or soiling weapon, a symbol of degradation. When someone is called a "shit," we imply he is worthless, to be held in contempt.

According to psychoanalytic findings, these early feelings about our eliminative processes explain why they are connected on the one hand with the feeling of achievement and love and on the other with hostility.

Not only is toilet training connected to our first experience of control over a bodily function, but also we learn, from the way we are toilet-trained, the attitude of our parents toward excrement— which is often one of shame and disgust. We learn also, since how parents feel about excrement is usually the way they feel about sex, their fears and guilts about sexual desire.

In Freud's book *Three Essays on the Theory of Sexuality,* written in 1905, he calls the anus one of the specialized parts of the body that is an "erotogenic zone." He also names the mouth, urethra, and genitals. He adds that the peripheral stimulation of these zones furnishes important contributions to the production of sexual excitation.

Where the anus is concerned as a sexual participant, it is clear that "disgust" stamps that sexual aim as a perversion, Freud says. He explains that certain regions of the body, such as the mucous membrane of the mouth and the anus, which may be a part of perverse sexual practices, "seem, as it were, to be claiming that they should themselves be regarded and treated as genitals." This claim is justified by the history of the development of the sexual instinct and is fulfilled in the symptoms shown in certain pathological states, he points out.

Like the labial zone of the vagina, the anal zone is well suited by its position to act as a medium through which sexuality may attach itself to other bodily functions, Freud maintains. The erotogenic significance of this part of the body is very great from the outset of life. For instance, the intestinal disturbances so common in childhood may affect the outlet of the intestinal canal and in turn cause hemorrhoids (little eruptions in the membrane that may symbolize the penis).

Children who make use of the susceptibility to erotogenic stimulation of the anal zone "betray themselves," Freud says, by holding back their stools until the accumulation brings about violent muscular contractions and, as the stools pass through the anus, they are able to produce powerful stimulation of the mucous membrane. In doing so, they "must no doubt cause not only painful but also highly pleasurable sensations," Freud adds.

One of the clearest signs of subsequent eccentricity, or nervousness, is to be seen when a baby obstinately refuses to empty his bowels when put on the pot—that is, when his mother wants him to—and holds back that function until he himself chooses to exercise it.

The retention of the fecal mass—which is thus carried out intentionally by the child in order to serve, as it were, as a masturbatory stimulus upon the anal zone or to be employed in his relation to the people looking after him—is also one of the roots of the constipation that is so common among neurotics, Freud states.

"Further, the whole significance of the anal zone is reflected in the fact that few neurotics are to be found without their special scatological practices, ceremonies, and so on, which they carefully keep secret," he adds.

Three years later, in 1908, in his classic paper "Character and Anal Erotism," Freud showed how some character traits originate in the warding off of certain impulses. He described persons who were "remarkable" for a regular combination of three peculiarities: "they are exceptionally *orderly, parsimonious,* and *obstinate.*"

He wrote:

Each of these words really covers a small group or series of traits which are related to one another. "Orderly" comprises both bodily

cleanliness and reliability and conscientiousness in the performance
of petty duties: the opposite of it would be "untidy" and "negli-
gent."

"Parsimony" may be exaggerated up to the point of avarice; and
"obstinacy" may amount to defiance, with which irascibility and
vindictiveness may easily be associated. The two latter qualities—
parsimony and obstinacy—hang together more closely than the
third, orderliness; they are, too, the more constant elements in the
whole complex. It seems to me, however, incontestable that all three
in some way belong together."

He said that in considering the experiences of the early childhood of such persons, one easily learns that they took a long time
to learn to control defecation. Even in later childhood, they
complained of isolated accidents relating to this function. As
infants, they seem to have been among those who refused to have
a bowel movement when placed on the pot because they found
an incidental pleasure in the act of defecation.

During the time of life known as the "sexual latency period,"
from the end of our fourth year to age eleven, we learn the
attitudes of shame, disgust, and morality. These feelings occur at
the expense of erotic feelings and constitute a barrier against the
later activity of our sexual instincts. Anal erotism is one of the
components of our sexual instinct that in the course of evolution
and in accordance with civilization's demands, have become use-
less for sexual aims.

Traits of orderliness, parsimony, and obstinacy generally appear
in those who were anal erotics as children and are a sublimation
of anal erotism. Cleanliness, orderliness, and reliability represent
a learned protection against an interest in things that are considered "dirty," "out of order," or "messy." A person who is very
obstinate probably behaved with great self-will as an infant when
it came to parting with his stools, daring to defy his mother when
he felt like it.

A slap on the buttocks (which are connected with the anal
erotogenic zone) is often used to make a child submissive. The
gesture and the words "Up yours!" is a very defiant one, an

unconscious challenge to what was once felt as a repressive parent when it came to toilet training.

I know of the instance of an eight-year-old girl whose father spanked her at the age of two for wetting her bed at night. She stopped thereafter but had difficulty in the opposite direction, according to her mother, who is a friend of mine, in that she became constipated and often went for days without evacuating her bowels. It was as though the child submitted to her father's strictures so completely that the opposite reaction set in. She overreacted out of her fear and her defiance.

Spanking, which is, we might say, brutality on the buttocks, may serve to erotize the anus in a hostile way. A teasing slap on the rear may be seductive. On the other hand, the exposure of one's rear end may be a gesture of contempt.

The connection between feces and money is seen in our use of the phrase "dirty money" or "filthy lucre." Freud says, in an article titled "On the Transformation of Instincts with Special Reference to Anal Erotism":

> In reality, wherever archaic modes of thought predominate or have persisted—in ancient civilizations, in myth, fairy-tale and superstition, in unconscious thoughts and dreams, and in the neuroses—money comes into the closest relation with excrement. We know how the money which the devil gives his paramours turns to excrement after his departure, and the devil is most certainly nothing more than a personification of the unconscious instinctual forces.

Freud also pointed out in this article, written in 1916, that there is a superstition that associates the finding of treasure with defecation. Treasure is usually buried in "dirt." In the early Babylon civilization, gold was called "the excrement of Hell." Freud theorizes it is possible that the contrast between the most precious substances known to man and the most worthless, which he rejects as "something thrown out," has contributed to the identification of gold with feces.

The correlation of feces and money in the unconscious is also made easy as the original erotic interest in the products of our own body lessens and interest in making money, a goal unknown to us in early childhood, appears. The earlier impulse, as it gives up its aim, is transferred in the sense of its psychic energy to the new desire to make money.

The concepts of feces (money, gift), child, and penis may replace one another in the thinking we do in the unconscious part of our mind. A baby thinks of his feces as his first gift which he bestows on his mother because he loves her. As he grows up, he learns that a penis brings the "gift" of a baby. We speak of a man "giving" a woman a baby. Also, it is a fantasy of childhood that a baby is created by the act of eating and is born through the bowels, going through the body, as food does.

A continually constipated person is showing his unwillingness to part with what his unconscious thinks of as a precious part of the body. We speak of feeling "uptight," meaning tense, unable to release feelings freely. Usually the constipated person is very tense and anxious. As a result, he may be ungiving in other ways.

A woman of twenty-five, in therapy because of an unhappy marriage, said of her husband, "He is such a stingy man. He won't spend a cent on me or himself." She added, almost in the same breath, "And he spends hours in the bathroom every morning." She unconsciously made the association between his stinginess and constipation.

According to Dr. Karl Abraham, colleague and friend of Freud's, who was a pioneer in the study of the formation of character, there are two kinds of anal pleasure: the pleasure of expelling and the pleasure of retaining. The former is the more archaic of the two. The child's mother forces him to relinquish this earlier pleasure. At first he experiences her command as a restriction. But soon he learns fresh possibilities of pleasure—new sensations of retention in the rectum and the narcissistic power of self-control. Thus retention (which serves as the model for the desire to "save"), originally a safeguard against the forbidden pleasure of expelling, becomes itself a pleasure. This safeguard and this new pleasure occur in the sphincter spasm—that is, in

muscular movements and sensations that exceed what is physiologically adequate.

Dr. Otto Fenichel, in his article "Organ Libidinization Accompanying the Defense against Drives" *(International Journal of
Psychoanalysis)*, speaks of "anal incorporation" which shows itself, for instance, in the paranoid's equating of persecutor and
feces, the infantile prototype of which is the enema, forced into
one by the mother, seen as the persecutor. He says:

> Incorporation is the object relation of pregenitality [before the
> child is aware of the function of the genitals]. All pregenital eroto-
> genic zones, therefore—insofar as the sensations arising from them
> are not merely autoerotic but are directed to objects—must be a
> point of departure for fantasies of incorporation. For this reason,
> oral, anal, and epidermal erotism has its counterpart in oral, anal,
> and epidermal introjection.

The child's interest turns from feces to mud, to dust, to sand,
to stones, then to all sorts of objects that can be "collected," and
finally to money. The desire to collect is anal in its erogenous
roots.

It may come as a surprise to the average individual, but it is
pretty much agreed among psychiatric authorities that despite the
varied range of objects that may form the basis of a collector's
activities, the objects themselves may occasionally be an unconscious representation of fecal symbols. In fact, collecting itself, in
some instances, may constitute an unconscious sublimation of a
primitive wish to hold on to products of the excremental function.
The man who collects depression glass, porcelain figurines,
stamps, or coins naturally takes pride and pleasure in these objects
—but the pleasure may be causally linked to the narcissistic joy
he found in his own feces during his infant period.

A spastic colon—that is, a readiness to react to various stimuli
with constipation or diarrhea—is either caused by anxiety or by
a sign of the patient's fixation on the anal phase of his libidinal
development (or perhaps both), says Fenichel.

If preoccupation with anality continues into adult life, someone may suffer from various diseases of the anus such as constipation or diarrhea, hemorrhoids, or cancer of the rectum.

Chronic diarrhea may be the bodily expression of emotions of disgust and hostility, as can its opposite, constipation. Patients who for years have used laxatives discover as a result of therapy that they can dispense with the laxatives as their bowels start to move without the need of an outside object forced into the body, either through mouth or anus, an act that has both sexual and aggressive overtones.

There is an illness jokingly called "honeymoon cystitis." It is the need to urinate frequently because of stimulation of the sexual organs. Some who are afraid of adult sexual pleasure may thus regress to the infantile sexual pleasure of urinating.

Hemorrhoids are often emotionally caused. Persons who suffer from them are usually very tense and anxious. One man, a writer, never had them in his life until faced by a deadline for a book. The pressure he felt under to get "the book out" was abnormal. Unconsciously he was regressing to infancy, refusing to be "forced" to "get out" his feces.

There are those who compulsively "must" have a bowel movement every morning or evening, or at both times, usually after a meal. Actually, there is no certain time each day that you must defecate.

In earlier times, mothers feared a child would be poisoned by his waste if he did not get rid of it every morning. This is fantasy. A human being can go days, even weeks, without evacuating his bowels and not harm himself. Nature will eventually take care of it. Anyone who believes he is "bad" if he does not have a bowel movement every day is still listening to the misguided voice of his mother in childhood.

A forty-year-old married man, an engineer by profession, came to me with an unusual physical complaint. He had decided to enter analysis because his bowel habits were driving him, as he put it, "up a wall."

Every morning, both at home and later at his office, he "had" to evacuate his bowels at intervals of half an hour, for five times, when he would then feel "completely empty." He kept accurate track of the time it took until he reached what he called the "empty stage," after five bowel movements. He had to achieve this "emptiness" before he could begin the day's work; otherwise he felt "evil." It is a fallacy, of course, to believe we can ever "empty" the contents of the lower intestine. That is impossible.

This man had seen internists who specialized in diseases of the gastrointestinal system and had undergone every test imaginable. Nothing was wrong with him physically. I asked, "How long have you had this pattern of evacuation?"

He confessed, "Ever since I was a little boy."

"Did your mother insist on it?"

"Quite the contrary," he said. "She never allowed me enough time in the bathroom to finish what I began. I always felt incomplete."

"So, as a little boy, you felt pushed out of the bathroom?" I asked.

"I certainly did," he said with emphasis. "There was only one bathroom in our house, and I had to share it every morning with my mother, my father, my oldest brother, and my younger sister. Mother was always chasing me off the toilet, saying, 'You're taking too long.'

"I would start off for school with this persistent feeling of unfinished business. Then at school I would head for the boy's room before classes began. And several times throughout the morning I would excuse myself from classes and go again. Until I felt finished."

"You made up for your mother's pressure on you by allowing yourself plenty of time to evacuate your bowels," I said.

"As if I was getting even?" He looked puzzled.

"There are few things more precious to us as children than our feces," I told him. "A child feels, at first, this is his only possession. He resents being told what to do with it. If a parent can toilet-train a child with gentleness and understanding, the child will slowly give up the feeling he is being deprived of something very important to him. But if a parent is harsh and unfeeling when it comes to toilet training, the child will suffer and carry the suffering into adulthood." Then I asked, "What do you think will happen to you if you don't defecate for a few days?"

"I'll fall ill and die," he said with conviction. "That's what my mother always told me."

"That is an old wives' tale," I said. "You are worrying needlessly about something that will never happen if you eat the correct foods."

He laughed in relief. "Should I tell my mother she's been living with a myth all these years?"

"Do you see her often?" I asked.

"My wife and I have dinner with her once a week. She lives nearby," he said. Then he added irritably, "I love her very much, but it's a damned nuisance having to save every Wednesday evening for her. Sometimes important business matters come up on a Wednesday night."

"And you can't break the date?"

"She'd feel hurt. She wouldn't understand," he muttered.

Here was a man still so attached to the mother of childhood that he was unable to break the dependency of Wednesday nights, even though he faced an occasional important business engagement. He loved his mother, but he also resented her hold on him. His toilet habits showed his defiance of her.

During therapy, his attitude toward his mother changed. He was able to tell her, when business came up on a Wednesday night, that he could not see her. He discovered she accepted this without protest. He also started to realize how harried she had been, as a young mother, with a fairly large family and not enough toilet facilities in the house.

He eventually was able to give up the fantasy that he could "empty" his bowels. He could begin his work in the morning even if he had not been able to defecate. He understood how, as a boy, he had been forced to hold in at home in the morning what he felt to be a necessary expulsion and that it had exploded in other ways.

The connection between anxiety and anal functioning was clearly demonstrated in the tragicomic experience of one man when I was a psychiatric resident at Bellevue Hospital in New York City in the late 1950s. It showed how a man may develop diarrhea when in danger instead of acting in an appropriate manner, as he emotionally withdraws from action into a dependent state. Instead of facing an emergency, in such a case the first impulse is to turn for help as he did when a child, performing an automatic act for which he once received praise from his mother.

One afternoon I was making the final rounds in a disturbed ward of the psychiatric section when I heard angry voices and shouts coming from one corner of the room.

I walked over to find out the cause of the disturbance.

I saw a man in his middle forties, evidently a new admission to the ward, with police and attendants standing around him. One attendant was trying to give him a hypodermic sedative to calm him down.

The man was protesting violently, "You can't do this to me. I won't take it. I must have some rights!" He turned to look at me and noticed my white coat. "Please help me, Doctor," he begged.

The plea in his eyes, the firm set of his chin, made me feel something had gone wrong, that his shouts held the tone of injustice being done. I said to the attendants in a quiet but firm voice, "Please bring this man to my office. I want to talk to him."

He drew himself away from their touch, said "I can walk by myself," and followed me into my small office.

I indicated a chair, saying, "Please sit there." I sat down in my chair behind the desk and directed him to tell me what had happened.

He looked at me gratefully. "Thank you," he said. "I've tried several times today to explain to *somebody*. You are the first one who will listen."

He started his story: "I left home at eight o'clock this morning. I live in Freeport, Long Island, about forty-five miles from here. I had to drive to the city for an important business appointment at ten o'clock. I was going to meet the head of a large corporation that was interested in buying my small business in Freeport. The meeting meant more to me than I can say. I was very nervous about it. I wanted it to go perfectly. My wife kissed me good-bye and said, 'Good luck, dear,' and I said, 'I'll sure need it.'

"On the way I got stuck in traffic. I hadn't realized how heavy it might be because I am not a regular commuter. I had left early, figuring the trip might take an hour, but allowing myself two hours. Well, the traffic was so bad that I just crawled along on the highway. It was getting later and later. As I neared the city, I suddenly felt an uncontrollable urge to go to the bathroom— to have a bowel movement. Naturally I couldn't, sitting there with cars barely moving. So I held it back and soon developed severe cramps.

"I should mention to you that I have a history of nervous diarrhea. Whenever I get upset or tense I seem to get the runs. It's difficult for me to control this tendency.

"As I drove over a bridge into the city, I spotted a hospital. I thought, 'I'll just dash in there and find a men's room.' I drove up in front of the hospital. There was a sign 'No Parking.' But by then the cramps were so severe I parked the car anyhow.

"I ran into the hospital, frantically looking for a men's room. I stopped a nurse. I gasped, 'Where is the men's room? I've got cramps.' She took me to the emergency room. But instead of showing me where the men's room was located, she said to an intern, 'This man has cramps. I think we should take his history. He may have appendicitis.'

" 'There's nothing wrong with me,' I protested. 'I just have to go to the bathroom. I've been driving for two hours and—'

"The intern ordered, 'Sit down and answer a few questions, please.'

"For the first time, I gave up. I could control myself no longer.

I sat down, and as I did, I let go in my trousers. There I sat, in the mess, the stench filling the room. But that didn't stop them from asking questions and filling out forms—my name, my address, my physical complaint. They wouldn't let me go. I begged them to release me. The damage was done. But they insisted on completing the forms.

"It was now ten o'clock. I had missed my appointment. I couldn't even show up late what with my trousers dirtied and smelling as I did. I was completely defeated. Like a bad child who has been punished for some unknown evil act.

"They finally let me go when they were convinced I wasn't dying of appendicitis. The nurse showed me to the men's room. I tried my best to clean up. Then I walked out of the hospital. I found a policeman about to ticket my car. I was desperate. I thought, 'What more can happen to me today?'

"I said to the policeman, 'Will you take five dollars to forget about a ticket?'

"He looked at me in contempt. He said, 'You're trying to bribe a police officer. I'll have to take you to the station house.'

"I sighed. I was now feeling like a character out of Kafka. It all made sense in a crazy kind of way.

"The next thing I knew I found myself in court, waiting for a judge. It was lunchtime and the judge had gone to eat. I waited for about an hour. I knew I should phone my business appointment and apologize for what had happened. But I didn't have the energy. I just sat waiting for the judge.

"When he finally arrived and I stood before him, I tried to explain what had happened. But he wasn't interested. He said in a nasty voice, 'Be quiet. I'm the one who talks here.' At that point, I really went out of my mind. I started to shout. I said, 'I have a reasonable story. No one will listen. Someone has to listen! I've missed a very important appointment!'

"The judge said to the policeman, 'Take this man to Bellevue. He's crazy.' I was led off, still trying to defend myself. I didn't want to be taken to Bellevue. I shouted until I was hoarse. But they drove me in a police ambulance to Bellevue. You walked in just as they were trying to give me the needle."

I sat listening, absolutely amazed at his story, realizing it *could* happen here.

He asked, "What should I do? Should I sue the city?"

"I don't think it will do any good," I said. "You'd better just chalk the whole thing up to experience."

He looked at me sadly and said, "What can I tell the man I was supposed to see at ten o'clock? I've lost my chance to sell the business."

"Not at all," I said. "People understand emergencies do arise." I handed him my telephone. "Why don't you call him and explain that an emergency came up. You don't have to tell him what it was. Ask him if you can have another appointment. If he really wants to buy your business, this man will see you."

He looked more grateful than ever. He said, "You are very understanding."

I left the office while he made the call. When I returned, he was standing by the door, waiting to say good-bye. He told me, "I feel you have saved my life. I have an appointment for tomorrow morning."

Then he smiled for the first time since I had seen him. He said, "I think I'll spend the night in the city at a hotel. I'll call my wife later and ask her to join me."

"Good luck." I put out my hand.

"I can never thank you enough, Dr. Stevens," he said, and was gone.

Here was an example, though extreme, of how tension can affect the excretory organs, which are closely related in very early life to moments of anxiety. This man, under the intense pressure of a business appointment that meant a great deal to him in terms of his future, was caught in traffic, unable to relieve himself, and developed severe stomach cramps, a psychosomatic symptom to which he was prone, that eventually drove him to disobey the law and offer a bribe to a police officer. In one sense, he was unconsciously punishing himself for carrying out the forbidden child-hood wish to evacuate his bowels at will.

Thus do our childhood desires, if not outgrown sufficiently, sometimes betray us into embarrassing, if not physically and psy-chologically painful acts.

9

THE SEXUAL ORGANS

Probably one of the most prevalent disturbances in the human body is the failure of the genitals to perform adequately in the act of sex. In men premature ejaculation, the inability to hold an erection or achieve an erection; and in women the inability to feel sensation in the vagina or to feel only pain, or inability to reach a climax are the cause of much anguish and unhappiness.

A thirty-year-old man came to see me, worried about his inability to maintain an erection. He said, "I get an erection, but then I lose it when I start to make love to the woman."

"When did this last happen?" I asked.

"The night before last," he said.

"Do you remember what you were thinking at the time the erection subsided?" I asked.

He was silent for a moment, then said, "I kept wondering what my mother would say if she saw me at that moment. I had the feeling she wouldn't like it."

"Do you always think about your mother when you are in bed with a woman?"

"Always." He sounded ashamed.

Then he added, in embarrassed tone, "My friends say I'm too attached to my mother. They say it not in scorn but in pity. They were the ones who advised me to see a psychiatrist."

"You discuss your sexual life with your friends?" I asked.

124

"It's been driving me crazy," he said. "I didn't know who else to talk to. But they've really been helpful. They pushed me to come here."

He told me he was an only son, that he had two older sisters. His father, who had died when he was ten, had been a very successful businessman but a strict and domineering parent. As a boy, he had always been frightened of him.

After his father's death, he drew very close to his mother, who substituted him for her dead husband, in a sense. She was the one to tell him the facts of life (which represents a kind of seduction by a parent of a child). He had always masturbated as a means of sexual outlet, not daring to have intercourse with a woman. He had lived with his mother until a year before when he rented his own apartment. He worked on Wall Street as the business manager of a prominent brokerage firm.

His first attempt at sexual intercourse had occurred six months earlier. He could hardly wait to get into bed with the young woman. They had embraced and kissed each other for hours in her living room at which time he was sexually aroused. But the moment they disrobed and threw the cover off her bed he felt his ardor diminish. He apologized, asked her to wait awhile, and they engaged in foreplay for an hour. He succeeded in arousing himself again. Then, almost immediately after he had entered her, he ejaculated. He was so embarrassed that he never saw her again.

During his treatment we worked, so to speak, to get his mother out of the bed. He slowly uncovered an underlying hostility to this woman to whom he felt so close in love and hate. He understood how, in her despair and loneliness, she had depended on him too intensely as an object of love. He had felt guilty every time he sexually desired a young woman, guilty at the thought that he was betraying his mother. Part of this guilt stemmed from his natural incestuous yearning for his mother—it was not one-sided.

As this man learned to accept his feelings and realize that, as a boy, it was normal for him to be attached to his mother but as an adult he had to relinquish some of the intensity of his feelings (by becoming aware of them), he was able to have an affair with a young female artist he met and successfully indulge in coitus. He married the girl, and a year after the marriage I received an announcement of the birth of their first baby.

Another man, twenty-eight years old, sought help because he was impotent though married. He was tall, blond, and one of the most handsome men I have ever seen. He was also a devout Catholic. He had served two years in the Korean War and was now a minor executive of a large airline. He had met a twenty-three-year-old stewardess, fallen in love, and married her.

He sat across from me in a chair, a pained expression on his face, and said, "I've been happily married for the past two months. But my wife wants the marriage annulled."

"Why?" I asked in surprise.

"Because she thinks I can't function sexually with her."

"What do you think?" I asked.

He sighed. "I suppose she's right."

"Do you love her?"

"Very much." His voice was fervent. "We had a romantic wedding at the Plaza with a reception for three hundred guests. Everyone said how happy we looked. As if we were made for each other."

"And then?"

"We went to Atlantic City on our honeymoon. We did not have sex before the wedding. We had decided we wanted to wait until we were married. But when we reached the hotel where I'd made reservations, I was so tired when we got into bed that I didn't even touch Loretta. She asked, 'Is something wrong?' I said, 'No, darling. I'm just exhausted. It's so late. Let's try tomorrow.' She drew to the other side of the bed and said 'All right.'

"But then in the morning I didn't feel like sex. I didn't even feel like hugging and kissing her. It seemed unnecessary now. Even when we got back to New York and our own apartment, I didn't feel sexy. She tried to arouse me, but it was no use.

"I was completely impotent with her. Even though I hadn't

been with other girls. Though I must admit that even when I was aroused, I didn't dare have sex. I thought I should wait until I got married. That's what my parents taught me."

He fell silent. I asked, "What have you done for a sexual outlet?"

He looked embarrassed, then said, "I've masturbated. It seemed the lesser of two evils. I didn't want to get any girl in trouble." He added defiantly, "I'm not a homosexual. That would be the final obscenity. I have a feeling I could be very potent. That's why I've come to you."

He insisted he was in love with his wife and wanted the marriage to succeed but she would not wait for him to confront and resolve his inner conflicts. She had grown increasingly hostile and refused to accept his temporary impotence. After four months of marriage, she had demanded an annulment.

He gave it to her reluctantly, knowing it would take time before he was able to come to emotional grips with his problems. He kept his appointments with me diligently. Slowly he uncovered hidden fears from his childhood. He had been brought up by an overpowering mother and father who had never allowed him to assert himself or his masculinity. An older brother who lorded it over him had contributed to his feeling of inferiority.

Gradually he began to understand how fearful he had been of his mother, how she had caused him to feel ashamed of his sexual desires, how she unconsciously wanted him to remain her "little boy." He saw, too, how he had gone along with her wishes, submitting to her dominance, never daring to assert his own independence.

After eighteen months of therapy, he met another stewardess, and he was able to have sexual intercourse. He did not want to marry her, and she shared his sentiments about formalizing their relationship. However, for the first time in his life, he was enjoying the feeling that his body was his own to do with as he wished, both in bed and out of bed.

The inhibition of sexual feelings may be experienced as shyness toward the opposite sex, or lack of interest in or disgust for the sexual act. Such emotions serve as defense against deeper sexual conflicts which usually remain repressed as long as sexual intercourse is avoided, or in extreme cases, if not brought to awareness by psychoanalytic treatment.

Impotence is a symptom that serves as protection against impulses and conflicts felt to be dangerous. Impotence may keep in repression sadistic fantasies, such as the one that the penis is a powerful, destructive organ that could harm or destroy a woman. This fantasy is a denial and projection of what Freud called castration anxiety, which, according to psychoanalysts, is the basic cause of all sexual inhibitions in men.

Premature ejaculation may vary in intensity and frequency. It may be characterized by the brevity of the sexual act or by a passive flow of seminal fluid minus the muscular rhythm of orgasm. A quick discharge of semen shows that the male sexual organ is engaging in a primarily eliminative function, that the man is afraid of his powerful genital urges. The quick discharge represents regression to an early phase of infantile functioning when the bladder was passively emptied without the need to overcome the tension of the sphincter.

According to psychoanalysts, premature ejaculation represents a fixation on "urethral eroticism." This fixation involves an unconscious identification in the psyche of semen with urine. This brings about the impulse to eliminate immediately as soon as pressure is felt. The climax of excitement is felt at the root of the penis and on the perineum rather than at the glans and in the shaft of the penis. This fixation also has its roots in enuresis and masturbation and therefore produces guilt and a feeling of inferiority.

The urinary eroticism of childhood leaves memory traces in the psyche of the adult that may be reawakened by sexual stimulation, as well as by blows to one's self-esteem, which lowers it, or praise, which heightens self-esteem. This explains why in instances of great danger or excitement there may be loss of the control of the bladder.

In no other area is the connection between the psychological and the physical so clear as in sexuality. Vaginal disturbances as a defense against sexual intercourse offer a direct example of a defense against sexual desire. Here a bodily organ is used to deny the conflict between the feeling of sensuality and a prohibition against it.

It has long been known that the sexual glands—the testes and the ovaries—exert a strong influence on temperament and behavior. Castration, the removal of the testes, as well as spaying, the removal of the ovaries, is used on farms to bring about temperamental changes in animals, and in the city, to "domesticate" cats and dogs.

In humans it has been observed that castration reduces virility not only because it leads to sterility but also because it produces bodily changes in sex characteristics and emotional changes that modify masculine traits. In women the early removal of the ovaries causes sterility and interferes with the development of physical and emotional female characteristics.

Experiments have shown the role of the sexual glands, or gonads, in the production of sexual hormones. Freud's theory that the disturbed chemistry of the sexually unsatisfied person produces anxiety and thus leads to other symptoms has been proved valid by biological studies. Psychoanalysis has shown that the maturation of the sexual function and the integration of the personality are closely intertwined.

In both men and women the sex glands are regulated by the pituitary gland. Through specific hormones the pituitary gland has an effect on the growth of our body as well as many aspects of metabolism. Through its "gonadotropic hormones" it stimulates the maturation, and controls the functions, of the testes and ovaries.

Under the influence of gonadotropic hormones, the testes produce the male gamates, or the spermatozoa, and one group of hormones, the androgens, whose chemical agent is testosterone, supposed to be responsible for virility. In the female there is a reciprocal interaction between the pituitary function and the ovaries which brings about a rhythmical change in the production of gonadotropins. This, in turn, affects the cyclic nature of the activity of the ovaries. The ovaries yield the female gametes, or ova, and two groups of hormones, which are produced in sequence: estrogens, which stimulate the maturation of the sex cells, and progestins, which provide for the growth and maintenance of the fertilized ova. Both types have a specific influence upon the sex characteristics and emotions of a woman.

The effects of the function of the sex glands in both men and women cannot be separated from the psychological factors connected with their experiences as a child, an adolescent, and an adult.

We are all born bisexual. Though the embryo is endowed with the potential of developing toward one sex, there is evidence that conditions may occur that interfere with its development toward that sex.

Through her breast-feeding or bottle-feeding and her physical care of the baby, the mother conveys attitudes that have a different significance for each sex. A boy develops during the early oral-receptive stage through identification with his mother, and if this is not an emotionally nourishing experience, it may add to the tendency toward bisexual reactions that oppose the goal of his psychosexual development as a man.

The signs of psychic bisexuality may be seen in the early phases of development before the genital period. A two-year-old boy normally shows signs of being self-assertive and independent, but if his psychosexual growth is thwarted, he is afraid to take new steps and remains dependent on his mother.

Psychoanalysts believe that the discovery of the female genitals, which lack a penis, is the trauma that leads the little boy to imagine his penis may be lost or taken away if he is "bad." The female genitals, which resemble the lips of the mouth, to him may appear as a devouring organ which could bite off and swallow his penis. Identification with the dangerous aggressor—his mother— is the most efficient defense against such a fear.

However, through this identification with a female, the boy may develop a "negative Oedipus complex." This means that instead of identifying himself with his father in the wish to love his mother, he wants to be loved by his father and to replace his mother. This wish reduces his fear of what to him are the destructive female genitals and also his fear of punishment by his father for being a rival for the love of his mother.

Homosexuals show this identification with the mother and the wish to replace the mother in their father's eyes (as well as bed). One boy of eight, who was the patient of a child psychoanalyst I know, clearly showed this tendency. He had been brought to the child analyst because he refused to go to school. When the analyst asked why, the boy replied, "I want to stay home and cook and clean house and be like Mommy. So Daddy will love me, too."

"Your father loves you," the analyst reassured him.

"My father hates me," the boy said, as though making a secret confession. "He thinks Mommy loves me better than she loves him. And that I love her better than I love him."

This boy had to protect himself against his fear of punishment by his father for being a rival for the love of his mother, to whom he had a childish but passionate attachment. Every time his mother left him alone in a room, he would run after her. One reason he played truant from school was that he did not want to leave her.

Girls who have too intense a masculine identification, after experiencing sexual impulses for their father and feeling the penis to be a "dangerous" organ, resolve their oedipal conflict by identifying with their father. Through an intense wish to have a penis, or the fantasy that she will grow one, the girl both represses her fear of the male organ and develops the hope that she is loved by her mother in the same way her mother loves her father and brother—if she has a brother.

One little girl, who was very closely tied to her mother, showed an almost paranoiac fear of men, including her father. At a stage when little girls regard their father as the love of their life, she would hide behind her mother's skirts whenever her father walked into the room. He had left home for two years, when the little girl was three years old, so that on his return he was a stranger to her (he had believed he was in love with another woman and walked out, only to beg his wife's forgiveness two years later, whereupon she took him back). Having been around only women (her mother and her maternal grandmother), the little girl was frightened to death of this tall, dark man who represented "maleness" and who terrified her when he wanted to kiss her. I predict this little girl will have difficulties accepting her feminine role when she grows up unless she receives some psychological help.

Dr. Margaret Gerard studied enuresis, or bed-wetting, in children, calling it a symptom of a bisexual tendency. She said both boys and girls who suffered enuresis experienced night terror in which they had the fantasy of attack by an adult of the opposite sex. The fear mobilized a "sadomasochistic excitation which is discharged by urination."

The sexually mature person has passed successfully through all the stages of psychosexuality—oral, anal, and phallic—and has reached the genital stage. Sexual maturity means that "the individual has learned to find gratification for his instinctual needs in the framework of his conscience," says Dr. Therese Benedek, psychoanalyst.

The sexual drives that flow through the adult human system are constantly being subjected to monitoring and control by our conscience. Our conscience, in turn, is significantly influenced by the mores of contemporary society so that our own personal moral standards are a kind of homogenous blend of environmental factors and our instinctual drives. The end result can be the impeding of mature sexual development. For example, anxieties and phobias caused by childhood conflicts or traumas can and do force sexual energy into infantile channels, thus retarding or warping its normal expression.

In essence, the development of an individual's personality is significantly influenced by the manner in which conflicts are resolved that occur between the stimuli of our basic and instinctive drives and the restrictive forces of parents and the accepted customs of the civilization in which we live.

Studies have shown that an unconscious wish may influence the production of hormones that regulate metabolism. For instance, if a boy has too deep a psychological identification with his mother, and wishes intensely to be like her, this tendency may increase the hormones that regulate his metabolism so that he unconsciously adopts a feminine way of walking and talking.

In considering some of the illnesses that afflict the sexual organs of women, it should be pointed out that the pain some girls suffer during their menstrual period is mainly psychological. Psychoanalysts note that women patients who have had intense cramps during the first few hours of the menstrual period find that the pain disappears as a result of therapy. One thirty-year-old woman told her analyst after four months of treatment, "It's unbelievable how my menstrual cramps have vanished. I used to have to go to bed the first four hours because I couldn't even walk. Now I don't get a single cramp."

Excessive menstrual cramps may indicate, for one thing, that the girl or woman is unconsciously resenting her feminine role, that she is reacting against what many women call "the curse" by showing her anguish in a bodily as well as psychic sense.

Dr. Fritz Mohr told of a girl in whom a series of strong conflicts during puberty resulted in an inhibition of pubescence. This lasted for ten years until psychotherapy uncovered the emotional basis. Then she started her menstrual period, her breasts developed, and a hairiness on her chin disappeared. Dr. Mohr concluded that endocrine factors had played a part "as a connecting link," but that psychic factors had caused the failure to develop and, when revealed, activated the endocrines, thus eliminating the inhibition to growth. He said, "Patients experience certain things, that is, certain experiences are discussed with them whereby a psychic inhibition is released, or a stimulus given, thus liberating the hormonal processes."

Infertility in a woman has deep psychological causes, the most obvious being her wish not to have children because of her deep fears. Realistically, childbearing may be dangerous no matter how many precautions are taken, and the task of bringing up a child is a difficult one, as most women realize in advance. If a woman looks on motherhood as a time-consuming and perilous time, rather than as a rewarding and challenging experience, she may suffer pain during her pregnancy and have a postpartum depression. There may be unconscious hostility toward the infant that she turns on herself.

In some cases, the fear of pregnancy and the angry impulses toward the fetus may act to suppress the hormonal processes that sustain pregnancy, and a spontaneous abortion results. Or toxic vomiting develops. Or a woman feels fatigued all the time and retreats to her bed.

Without knowing why, a woman fearful of pregnancy may develop strange panics, even suicidal impulses. Or she may become temporarily psychotic. She will feel guilty because she has failed in her maternal function, one she unconsciously does not want to perform. Dr. Benedek points out, "It seems that the onrushing metabolic processes of pregnancy recharge the developmental conflicts with such intense emotions that they overwhelm the ego and render it helpless in the face of the most significant integrative task in a woman's life."

A woman in her late thirties, who had been married eight years, came to me complaining that she could not have children though she and her husband had continually tried.

She said, tears in her long-lashed blue eyes, "He blames me. He says I am the sterile one. That I don't want babies."

Husband and wife had been examined by physicians who found no physical reason why they should not become parents. As a last resort, the wife decided to go into therapy.

"My mother had four children and my husband's mother had five, so there has been no problem of sterility in either of our families," she said. She paused, regarding me with a sharp, probing stare, then added, "As a matter of fact, my mother had two miscarriages. So she could have had six children in all."

"How old were you when she had the miscarriages?" I asked.

"I was ten years old the first time, and twelve years old the second," she said.

"So you were aware of what was happening when your mother lost the babies," I said.

"Very much so," she said, her lips moving nervously. "I heard my mother screaming in pain, both times. I was the one who called the doctor." Her voice became a trifle shrill.

"How did you feel?" I asked.

"Frightened to death," she admitted. "I thought my mother was going to die."

And fearful, too, that if she were ever to become pregnant, she might die. She had the fantasy that to bear a baby meant death. She also recalled that as a little girl she had been very jealous of her mother's ability to have babies. She possessed a strong unconscious wish to have her father's baby, a wish she dared not admit to herself, though it is the normal, natural wish of every little girl. It is a wish that prepares her for motherhood as she transfers her erotic desire from her father to a more appropriate man.

After a year of therapy, during which she came to understand how her deep-rooted fears had developed to the point that they had helped set up physical barriers within her own reproductive processes, this wife became pregnant. She told me the news with stars in her eyes. She thanked me profusely.

I said, "Thank yourself for having the courage to face some of your deeper conflicts. You deserve the credit."

"My husband is *so* happy," she said. "And, as you know, so am I."

She was reaping the reward of the work she had put into the task of examining hidden terror and rages which, when exposed to the light of reason, proved not so monstrous after all.

Hysterectomies in which fibroid tumors are the cause of the loss of the uterus may symbolize unconscious pregnancy fantasies.

One woman referred to the tumor, half wistfully, half in mockery, as "my phantom baby." A growth inside the body may symbolize either baby or penis, or as part of Freud's "triad," a withheld stool of infancy.

There are cases of phantom pregnancies in which a woman imagines she is having a baby. The wish is for a baby by her father, an act that is forbidden her, but the wish is so strong it overcomes all rational thinking.

The story of Anna O. is the most famous case involving a phantom baby. She was a patient of Dr. Josef Breuer in Vienna in 1881. When he ended his therapeutic psychological treatment after eighteen months, she imagined she was having his baby. She had reacted on his last visit as though she were going through the pangs of childbirth, throwing herself on the floor and writhing as though in the pain of birth, and claiming he was the father of her child.

Breuer, a very puritanical, moral man, was horrified and fled the house. Later, when he told his young colleague, Dr. Sigmund Freud, what had happened, Freud interpreted the phantom pregnancy as the desperate wish of this hysterical young lady, upon feeling abandoned by her therapist, to have his baby—as in her unconscious she had wished as a little girl to have the baby of her father. Little girls normally want to have their father's baby, a wish they give up within the course of natural psychosexual development, as they transfer this wish to a man outside the family, a more appropriate father.

Cancer of the breast and of the uterus are frequently caused by deep psychic conflicts. Breast cancer symbolizes unconscious castration of the breast, which is a protruding object like the penis, and cancer of the uterus may symbolize a rejection of femininity. Incidentally, when deep conflicts occur, their roots are always in childhood. When sexuality is rejected, it is based on the tabooed, incestuous love for the parent of the opposite sex. This is the reason the person must punish himself through physical illness. If it were normal, adult sexual desire, there would be no need to reject it and no need to punish the self.

Georg Groddeck, called the father of psychosomatic medicine, in his book *The Unknown Self* said of cancer:

> We know so little about cancer that we cannot afford to ignore the possible contribution of our powerful unconscious. Do many people know, for instance, why cancer tissue grows so fast? It does so because the body supports the rapid growth by tremendous increase of the blood supply to the malignant tissue. Why? It sounds like a deliberate attempt, unconscious to be sure, to destroy ourselves, just like committing suicide. . . . If we take unconscious forces into consideration . . . we might be able to explain it.

Groddeck related the development of a cancer in the body to the growth of a baby, theorizing it might be caused by the wish to have a baby, even in men.

Tissue changes may develop "as complications at the site of a conversion," state Dr. G. L. Engel and Dr. A. H. Schmale, pioneers in psychosomatic studies. They point out that the unconscious resolution of an inner conflict may cause changes in body tissue, resulting in cancerous growth. The goal of the processes that produce these physical changes is to relieve the internal psychic pressure of a powerful wish connected to an instinctual drive. The physical illness thus is sought unconsciously, not consciously.

Menopause is supposed to bring depression, but the depression that occurs during menopause is only severe if the woman has been depressed all her life. Otherwise she will not be unduly affected by it.

Two physicians, Dr. C. B. Farrar and Dr. R. M. Franks, in their article "Menopause and Psychosis" in the *American Journal of Psychiatry* in 1931, summarizing the factors in the development of abnormal and nervous conditions during menopause, wrote:

> There is . . . the age-old tradition which unduly exaggerates the morbific potential of the climacteric. . . . There is a widespread assumption that trouble may be looked for when the change of life comes, just as many people expect to be seasick when they cross the

ocean. This state of the feminine mind in general is unfortunately
encouraged all too often by the medical profession and the opinion
is too readily expressed that difficulties of all sorts occurring during
the rather wide span of the transition years are to be attributed to
the menopause. . . . In all ways the menopause has come to be a
bugbear which it does not deserve to be. It has been artificially
tinctured with fears and apprehensions; and the fears and apprehensions themselves lead to troubles for which the menopause as such
is not primarily responsible . . .

A number of women exhibit neurotic, somatic, and occasionally psychotic symptoms which, because they occur during the
transitional period of menopause, are often attributed to it as the
basic or underlying cause. But psychoanalytic study of such
women reveals that the symptoms that appear aggravated during
menopause already existed in the lives of such women. They held
strong unconscious wishes to be a man which interfered with their
natural childbearing and child-raising functions, whereas women
who had no such conflicts were able to direct the psychic energy
that previously went into bearing and raising children to new
interests, taking on a career, expressing an artistic urge, or doing
social work. As Dr. Benedek said, the climacterium, in a psychological sense, could be thought of as "a developmental phase" if
the woman has fulfilled her feminine role in life up to that point.

One woman of fifty-one years of age, whose life had been a
happy one with her husband of thirty years and her son and
daughter, who were married, found she did not feel depressed, as
did the rest of her friends, when she reached menopause. She felt
instead a new burst of energy.

She decided she would do something she had always wanted to
do—become a real estate broker. In a sense, she found a new
career, realizing her days of bearing babies were past and content
in the fact she had done all she could to raise two children. Her
husband was delighted that she had acquired a new interest and
praised her highly for her decision to start a career at her age.

With men, too, though their reproductive function is not
ended, during the climacterium they may feel a diminishing of

the sexual urge. The way in which a man responds to his waning sexual potency depends upon his personality. The mature man will take it in stride, finding compensations in his work, in sports or hobbies, or in his family. But some men may respond to a basic insecurity about their potency with deep depression, complete loss of sexual vigor, even regression to a sexual perversion (the "dirty old men" who seduce young boys).

While prostate trouble may be a symptom of this sexual insecurity, I also believe that hypertrophy (enlargement of the prostate gland) in many cases is a result of men in their youth restraining their sexual desire too often, withholding ejaculations because of the fear of pregnancy, having constant erections that are frustrated, or indulging in foreplay for too long a time before ejaculating.

There is no reason why a man cannot function sexually after a prostate operation. It is just that many older men, lacking a courage they never really felt, lose their potency in a psychological sense.

When I was a resident at University Hospital in Geneva, Switzerland, I recall making the rounds one day on a ward of cardiac cases. In our group were the chief of services, the assistant chief of services, the resident, and a young intern.

We stopped beside the bed of a very charming white-haired gentleman in his early sixties who was recovering from a heart attack. He said to the chief of service, in a courtly manner, "I'd like to ask one question, now that I have recovered and am going home. Am I supposed to have sexual intercourse with my wife?"

The chief of service replied, "How do you feel about it?"

The old gentleman shrugged his shoulders and said, "I don't know. That's why I'm asking you."

The chief of service turned to his assistant and asked, "What would your advice be?"

"I think if he feels it is all joy and no work, by all means, he should go ahead and have sexual intercourse," replied the assistant chief of staff, a man in his early fifties.

The chief then turned to the resident and asked, "What would you say?"

The resident, in his early thirties, replied, "I think even if it's half work and half joy, I would tell him to go ahead and have sex."

The chief of staff then turned to the intern, who was in his middle twenties, and asked, "And how do you feel about it, young man?"

The intern thought for a moment, then replied, with a tinge of distress, "Well, if it was all work—I'd be asked to do it!"

Everyone roared with laughter. It is universal in hospitals throughout the world that the period of internship holds an unbelievable amount of work.

If a person who has had a heart attack is emotionally able to enjoy sex, it may be harder on his heart not to have intercourse. Anything may burden the heart if it causes anxiety. Rather than depriving himself of sexual pleasure, if a man with a physical ailment has been accustomed to the enjoyment of sex, he should continue to get pleasure from it as long as he is able.

He should adopt a positive mental attitude about sex. After all, the libido is not supposed to die of old age. It can be as powerful at eighty as at eighteen. One's attitude toward sexual matters is as important as one's attitude toward all the various life situations that confront the individual. If a person is privately convinced that he is incapable of performing some act, the chances are relatively certain that his futility will be proved by events. Faith and confidence on the part of the patient are important factors in helping a physician heal physical ills and a psychiatrist in healing psychic wounds. This same element of strong belief naturally carries over into sexual activities. Its presence is usually a contributing factor to successful performance and enjoyment; its absence can frequently result in frustration.

10

LEGS, ANKLES, AND TOES

The foot is often described symbolically as responsible for mistakes: putting the wrong foot forward, making the wrong step, putting your foot in your mouth. Some people unconsciously cripple their extremities so they lose the use of them and do not have to face conflicts that are threatening.

One day a young man walked into my office. He told me he was twenty-two years old and a graduate student in history at Columbia University. He said, "I feel I need help because I'm having great trouble with girls."

"In what way?" I asked.

"I never date the girl I really want and have to settle for second best," he said.

"Why do you think you do that?"

"I'm afraid to ask the girls I really want to take out."

He was tall and built like an athlete and had very prepossessing features. His manner seemed disarming, and there was a quiet charm about him. It appeared, on the surface, that any young woman would be delighted to have him as her escort.

"What are you afraid of?" I asked.

"I'm afraid they won't like me, once they get to know me," he said.

We talked of his feelings as an adolescent when he also was afraid to ask the girls he liked to high school dances. He said, "So

I picked the unattractive, dull ones. And never had fun with them."

He felt shy and unsure with girls, that he could never make a sexual advance unless he had a lot to drink, which interfered with his potency. He discussed his relationship with his parents, who were themselves very inhibited in any show of affection so that he had grown up feeling that to display affection was "bad."

After several sessions, during which he discussed his feelings further, he came in one morning, his eyes shining with excitement.

He said, "I have a date tonight with a girl I've wanted to take out for months. It took all my courage to ask her for a date. She's in my history class. I've adored her from a distance. I said to myself yesterday, 'What can you lose? Go ahead. Ask her out.' I did. And she said she'd go. It's tonight! Isn't that great?"

"Fine." I thought he had gained confidence enough to ask the girl of his choice for a date.

Two days later at his next session, he limped into my office. His face was dejected. He sat down, with obvious pain, in the chair.

"What's the matter?" I asked, concerned.

"You know that date I told you about? The girl I had wanted to take out for so long? Dating girls I really didn't care about though I really wanted her?"

"Yes," I said. "You told me at your last session that you had asked her out."

"You'll never believe what happened!" He looked as though he were about to burst into tears.

"Tell me."

He sat back in the chair, his hand over his forehead for a moment, as though to blot out all memory. Then he began:

"She said to pick her up at eight. That afternoon I took a nap to feel refreshed. I overslept. It was six thirty when I woke. I dressed in a rush, raced out of my apartment on West Seventieth Street. She lives in Queens with her aunt. Her home is in Omaha. She had given me her address and telephone number and told me which subway to take. I grew up in Austin, Texas, so I don't know New York too well.

"I got on the right subway. On the way I discovered I had left her address and phone number on the bureau in my apartment. But I remembered the subway stop in Forest Hills. I decided to go there, get off the subway, and ask, in all the apartment houses near the subway—she said she lived not far from the exit—if a Nancy O'Brien lived there.

"I asked every doorman in the vicinity if he knew a Nancy O'Brien. I described her. She's a pretty, slim blonde, about medium height, with long straight hair and large blue-gray eyes. The doormen didn't know her. They shrugged their shoulders hopelessly. They could give no help. I couldn't even look up her number in the telephone book because the phone is listed in the name of her aunt, and I had no idea of her aunt's name. It could be the same as hers, but there are a million O'Briens in the directory. So I decided to take the hour's ride back to my apartment and call her from there to tell her what happened.

"On the way back, sitting in the subway car, I suddenly developed a terrible cramp in my right calf. It was so painful I could hardly step off the train. Then my left calf got a cramp, too, so that both feet hurt. I made it to my apartment, walking very slowly. When I looked at the clock, I saw it was eleven.

"I grabbed the piece of paper with her address and phone number on it, picked up the phone, and dialed the number. She answered. Even her 'hello' sounded cold. I said, 'Nancy, I'm terribly sorry I'm so late. I left my apartment in a hurry and forgot to take your address and phone number. I tried to find you in Forest Hills, but every doorman I asked said there was no Nancy O'Brien in the apartment. I had to come all the way home and get the address and phone number. Will you wait for me if I start out again?'

"She said, 'Forget it! Tonight and forever!' and hung up.

"You can imagine how terrible I felt. But I was so tired, and my feet hurt so, that I simply toppled on the bed and slept eight hours straight."

He took a deep breath, then went on: "The next day my feet felt better so I made a date with another girl, one I didn't particularly like. I had taken her out once before.

"She lived in the other direction, in the north Bronx. When I started out that evening to pick her up at her home, my calves again started to hurt so much that I had to call her and break the date. But at least I wasn't three hours late. And she understood. She didn't hang up on me. She gave me a rain check."

"Do your legs hurt now?" I asked.

"They do. But I was determined to get here. To tell you what happened."

I sent him for X rays, wanting to make sure nothing was physically wrong. The X rays showed there was no neurological reason for his pain and discomfort. His legs were perfect, physically.

At the following session I explained, "There seems to be no physical cause for the sudden pain in your calves."

"Then why do they hurt?" he asked.

"Did you ever have such a pain before?" I asked.

"I don't think so," he said.

"What were your thoughts that evening when you started out for Queens?" I asked.

"I was very excited at the thought of taking out 'the' girl. A girl I really cared about. But I was also scared to death of what she might think of me. And I took the nap so I would be in top form. So I wouldn't be tired."

"And yet you arranged it so that you left the apartment in a rush, forgetting to take her address and phone number. You tried to make sure you *wouldn't* see her," I said.

"I didn't do it deliberately," he said in alarm.

"No. Unconsciously," I explained. "The part of you that was frightened, that didn't think you would measure up as a man, took over. It made you oversleep, forget to take the slip of paper. And it punished you afterward by incapacitating your legs. It made it impossible for you to return to Queens that night, even if Nancy had consented to see you. It also made it impossible for you to keep the date the following night."

"Why was I punishing myself?" he asked.

"Perhaps you felt so attracted to her that you feared she might prove sexually stimulating. This went against what you believed your parents would approve."

"But how does that explain my pain the next night?"

"What were your feelings that night?" I asked.

He looked at me in surprise. He said, "Do you know they were different from the first time I went out with that girl? I was thinking that this time maybe I would make out with her. Last time I only kissed her good night. But I was so upset by what had happened the night before that I thought I would have sex with this other girl."

"So your unconscious again took over and made it impossible," I said.

"Would you believe it?" There was a look of awe on his face.

"Never underestimate the power of the unconscious," I said.

This young man remained in therapy eighteen months, talking about his hidden fears and angers. He was what psychiatrists call a passive-aggressive personality. This means passive on the out-side, aggressive on the inside.

Through the years he had become resigned to his parents' restrictive hold on him. He never dared to think for himself, seldom even tried to challenge them—though inwardly he was in constant rebellion against their stringent dictates. In a compensatory action, he punished *himself* for his inward rebellion rather than bring himself to defy them openly.

However, as he began to throw off the shackles of past restraints during the give-and-take process of therapy, he no longer crippled his legs. He finished his graduate work, became a teacher of history in a private school in Westchester, met a young woman who taught English at the school, married her, and today they have two children. As far as I know, his legs never bothered him again. They had served their purpose that one emotionally stormy night, as they protected him from a situation that menaced his manliness.

Sometimes accidents serve as the unconscious way of trying to avoid what a person considers a greater danger to his survival.

One husband, whose wife was asking for a divorce, though he did not want one because he was still in love with her, packed his valise and prepared to leave the house forever. Walking to the garage to get his car, he tripped over a large stone in the driveway and broke his ankle. This was his unconscious way of delaying the divorce. He had to remain at the house, since his wife could not turn him out with a broken ankle. The accident did not really help his cause, since his wife was adamant when he could once again walk, that he leave.

Illnesses of the foot include varicose veins, flat feet, arthritis of the joints, and bunions—growths on the feet, often caused by wearing improper shoes. Then there is athlete's foot, a very prevalent disease in America. It is a fungus infection, a ringworm, frequently picked up around community showers or public pools. Those who aren't fussy about personal cleanliness are more apt to get it than others. Once the infection sets in, it persists beyond the realm of reason.

Athlete's foot was so named because athletes, who use common showers, often suffered from it. It has become a widespread, uncomfortable skin condition that hinders people from proper use of their very much needed toes.

Athlete's foot can be used as an excuse for not being able to go places because of pain or embarrassment over the smell of the ointment (in former days it was treated with tincture of gentian violet which turned the toes purple). The illness may thus be used to keep one from walking to places or situations that are painful.

If you dry your toes carefully and always use powder between the toes, there is no reason to catch athlete's foot no matter where you take a shower. As with most illnesses, if you think enough of yourself to take care of yourself, you will not succumb to it.

Then there are those people who have a history of weak ankles. If the problem is not caused by an organic deficiency, it may be related to some unconscious wish not to be able to walk. There are also people who turn their ankles as they encounter every hazard in the street, be it banana peel or pebble. They are among the accident-prone, those who unconsciously seek accidents because they are beset by inner conflicts.

An adolescent girl of fifteen was sent to me by her parents because she was always tripping over small objects and spraining or breaking her ankle.

"You'd think she was a football player," said her mother aggrievedly over the telephone, as she made an appointment for her daughter to consult me.

At the appointed hour in walked a very plump young lady, with long brown hair and round gray eyes. I say "walked" in, though the process was more akin to "thumping" in. She was so plump that it must have been difficult for her to see her feet. This factor alone could contribute to her tendency to trip over every random object or obstacle.

She sat down, managing to walk across the office without injuring her ankles. She looked at me dumbly, almost fearfully, as if she expected me to attack her physically.

I smiled and said softly, "Please make yourself comfortable. Your mother tells me that you have a problem about falling over things and injuring your ankles."

She looked at me sadly. "I never seem to see things that lie in my way," she admitted.

"Why do you think you hurt yourself so much?" I asked.

She shrugged her heavy shoulders. "I really don't know. Maybe it's because I don't care what's in front of me. So it's there. So I trip over it."

"Perhaps, then, because you can't walk while your ankle heals, you have an excuse for not doing things you don't want to do?"

She looked at me with a sudden, knowing expression in her eyes. "Is that it?" she queried.

"It could be one reason why you continually hurt yourself," I said. "There are others."

Suddenly tears welled up in her eyes. "Most of the time I don't want to go out of the house," she exclaimed in a burst of defensive rage.

"Why?" I asked.

"Because I'm ashamed to be seen! Look at me. I'm so fat," and the tears streamed down her cheeks.

"Why don't you lose weight?" I asked.

"I've tried. I've tried." It was an anguished wail. "But I'm always so hungry, I can't stop eating."

It was obvious that she ate because of psychic hunger, and she crippled herself so that she wouldn't have to be seen by anyone. Also, in this fashion, she made it impossible for herself to go out on dates and risk being rejected by boys because of her physical appearance.

Over the next few weeks, she talked more about her insatiable need to eat, and we worked out a manageable diet for her, one that decreased greatly her caloric intake. She started to lose weight gradually, the way it should be lost. One day she charged into my office and proudly announced, "I've lost the twentieth pound! Isn't that great?"

"And you haven't hurt your ankle since you started coming here. That's important, too," I told her.

Once again she wanted to be seen and to go places. She went out on dates. She spoke of one boy she liked very much who told her that he liked plump girls and did not mind her excess pounds. She was now far less overweight than when I first saw her; she did not even mind appearing in a bathing suit.

Here is an example of how someone may cripple an ankle unconsciously as a way of escape from internal conflicts. This young girl was assailed by a great deal of hidden rage at her parents for both real and unreal reasons. They spoiled her one minute, criticized her the next. As a child, she had been subject to temper tantrums, able to rebel openly. But with the onset of adolescence, she controlled and denied to herself all signs of her anger. It erupted, however, in the need to overeat, and the constant spraining and breaking of her ankles, as though in this way she would get revenge on her parents. Once she was able to understand the ramifications of and reasons for her compensatory actions, she felt far more at ease in her home.

There is also the problem of ingrown toenails. This may seem like a minor affliction, but it can be very painful and can keep people from walking. I knew of one woman who would constantly pick at her toenails, infecting them so badly that she could not get around. She had been married twenty-one years, had no children, and could not make up her mind to get a divorce from a husband she merely tolerated.

It was as though she were picking away at her husband, and at herself, as she talked about her inability to reach the decision to leave him. "I vacillate back and forth—to get out, to stay," she said. "One minute I feel I must pack and leave. The next, I feel sorry for him and determine to try to make a go of it, no matter how I feel."

"In a way, you are unconsciously fighting to stay, as you infect your toenails. This prevents you from walking out," I told her.

"I know that much of the time I want to remain with John," she confessed. "After all, we've been married a long time."

"Do you argue about many things?" I asked.

"It isn't that," she said almost hopelessly. "John never argues with me. He always gives in. It's—it's—well, he bores me."

"Do you have any outside interests?"

She sighed. "Once I thought I was a fairly good commercial artist. But I gave up painting when we got married."

"Why don't you start painting again?" I asked.

Having an outside interest does not solve inner conflicts, but it does help to invest energy in a creative pursuit rather than in endless complaints while you are solving the inner conflicts.

Subsequently this woman went out and purchased canvases,

paints, and an easel. She began to spend hours in her "studio," a room in her large house she converted into a workshop. At the same time, she continued her visits to me, working through some of her feelings about her husband, many of which she realized stemmed not from any inadequacy of his but from her own unreasonable demands.

She was still expecting him to be the Sir Galahad of her adolescent dreams, but as she trained herself to accept him as a human being, she found him far less boring. She started to engage him in conversation about his business (he owned a large manufacturing plant), expressing a personal interest in his daily activities— something she had never done before. He, in turn, admired her artwork and encouraged her to take lessons and become even more proficient.

She discovered almost automatically one day that she had not picked her toenails in months. She said to me gratefully, "Thank you for helping me understand many things. Things I was evidently trying to duck away from."

We can never deny what disturbs us most deeply. It will inevitably make its presence known, through physical illness, if in no other way.

11

THE SKIN

Have you ever wondered why you shake hands when you meet someone for the first time? Or again upon meeting someone you like? And why the refusal to shake hands is a gesture of dislike and hostility?

It is because the feel of skin on skin between two people signifies trust and friendship. The "touch" is reassuring, tells of warm feelings. It is a symbol of closeness in the psychic as well as physical sense.

A pat on the shoulders or a gentle touch on the cheek or buttocks, as skin meets skin, also are gestures of liking. The gentle stroking of an arm or hand is a gesture of love. The skin is one of the body's senses that is most significant when it comes to feelings of love or hate.

Any disruption or eruption of the skin, therefore, indicates strong feelings within a person. Many skin diseases are so resistant to any form of treatment other than psychotherapy that dermatologists are becoming more and more aware that psychic conflicts are involved when acne or eczema or allergies persist.

That skin has deep sexual implications is seen in the words of poets who praise the beauty of the skin of the woman they love, the "pure white flesh," "the skin soft to the touch." Advertisements on TV besiege the feminine watcher from morning until midnight about the need to keep skin clean and pure and soft so that a woman will be attractive to a man.

The skin is that part of the body that cannot be hidden and thus that part that disappears least readily from awareness. Because it is exposed, there is apt to be preoccupation with it as though it were the body's showcase. Our feelings are revealed through the skin. We blush—that is, our skin reddens—when we are shamed or embarrassed. We pale when we are afraid. We get goose pimples from the cold. We flush and perspire from the heat.

A woman in her middle forties, married, with two daughters and a considerate husband who gave her all the money she wanted, was totally and completely preoccupied with the ills of her body, from head to toe. When she walked into my office, I saw a tense, nervous, rather plump woman of average height, with a worried look on her once-pretty face.

She sat down, clasped her hands together anxiously, and slowly began to talk. "I came here because I know I bug my husband, my daughters, and all my friends with my constant complaints. I need your help. Doctors say there is absolutely nothing wrong with me physically."

"What hurts you?" I asked.

"Everything!" She threw up her hands in despair.

"Could you be more specific?"

"Well, most recently my skin started to itch, so I scratched it, trying to relieve the itching. One doctor gave me some ointment which cleared it up for the moment. I felt so relieved. I felt my ovaries jump!"

I had never heard a connection between a skin ailment and a sexual feeling put so directly before, but I said nothing about it. Instead I asked, "Did your skin break out at certain times?"

"It seemed to get worse every time I had to go into a supermarket," she confessed. "It would turn red, then hurt, then itch. I also felt like fainting every time I had to shop for food."

"Do you have any idea why?

She hesitated, then said, "I just didn't feel right going into a supermarket and spending all the money I wanted on anything I wished to buy."

"Why didn't you feel right?"

Tears came to her eyes. "I thought of when I was a child and we were so poor that we couldn't buy the food we needed. Many a time I went to bed hungry. Now my mother and father are dead and buried and I feel it isn't right for me to have what they couldn't have."

Here was an odd situation involving a woman tortured by guilt feelings because she feared that her life might be a happier one than her parents had experienced. I said to her, "You don't have to live with the dead. You should be able to leave your past behind. Your mother and father would be pleased to know you are able to afford the luxuries they could not give you. Why punish yourself for a pleasure?"

Her mouth opened wide. She said, "I never thought of that."

"You have always felt too guilty to use reason," I said.

She remained in therapy for a period of a year, during which time she spoke of buried feelings about her mother and father, gradually uncovering the reasons for her guilt, including a passionate attachment to her father, who spoiled her, and an intense hidden hatred for her mother, based on her oedipal conflict.

The conscious reason for her fear about shopping in a supermarket, and her consequent skin outbreak, was her feeling of guilt at the thought of enjoying things denied to her parents. But the *unconscious*, stronger reason was her feeling as a child that her father loved her better than he did her mother, and this guilt she could not bear.

Her mental attitude, in the process of a year's treatment, changed to a healthy outlook that enabled her to overcome her guilt, to make and keep friends whom she previously drove away with her complaints, and to enjoy the riches of life that her husband was able to give her. Her skin had completely cleared up.

Physicians have long noted the relationship between skin diseases and nervous disorders. One doctor friend recently remarked to me, "Skin cases drift into my sanitarium for nervous diseases like driftwood and debris on the seashore." Under hypnosis, skin diseases have been cured with suggestion they are cured, and also reproduced when that suggestion was given.

There are men who develop skin infections after an illicit affair, but not after sexual intercourse with their own wives, indicating the eruption of the skin may be displacement of guilt. One psychiatrist described the case of a young girl who "had a petting party with her fiancé in the apartment of her aunt. Unfortunately the aunt surprised the young couple. The next day violent swelling and pain developed in the labia [of the girl]. When this girl came to the office, very much disturbed, she showed an extensive herpes genitalis [skin outbreak on her genitals]—a vasomotor neurosis."

Freud pointed out that in the case of components of the sexual instinct that involve pain and cruelty, the skin becomes an erotogenic zone. He said, "The skin, which in particular parts of the body has become differentiated into sense organs or modified into mucous membranes . . . is thus the erotogenic zone *par excellence.*"

It seems probable, he added, that any part of the skin, and any sense organ, "probably, indeed, *any* organ can function as an erotogenic zone, though there are certain particularly marked erotogenic zones whose excitation seems to be secured from the very first by certain organ contrivances," referring to the genitals, the mouth, and the anus.

Physicians in the old days warned that certain kinds of baths not be given those who seemed sexually very excitable because the potent skin stimulus acted like an aphrodisiac. Cold and heat may stimulate skin erotism in a way that differs from person to person —some find cold very exciting, others feel seductive when it is warm. Mothers sometimes blow on burns or blisters, as though to cool the pain.

The most intimate connection of the skin with sexuality appears in the act of tickling. Many languages use the same word for "tickle" and "sexual intercourse." In some folk traditions, if a girl is ticklish she is still considered a virgin. The giggling of girls in puberty is related to a displaced tickling in the throat. When a parent tickles a child, whether or not he knows it, he is sexually stimulating the child.

One woman, during her psychoanalysis, recalled that her father would often tickle her in the ribs when she was a little girl. She said, "I loved it but at the same time I would feel a sense of panic and fear. I would scream in both horror and delight."

"As though it were a rape of the ribs," commented the psychoanalyst.

Itching may be a sign of impatience. But there is also what is known as nervous itching, or pruritus, which occurs most frequently in the erogenous zones, in the vulva or anus or scrotum or the urethral orifice. Scratching during the attacks gives marked relief and pleasure. In one case a man's scratching himself resulted in an orgasm, thus proving the pruritus was the equivalent of masturbation in the unconscious. In another instance a woman who had eczema all over her body, so that she was constantly scratching, also had orgasms via the scratching. In a third instance a woman who suddenly got pruritus went from physician to physician in despair because they could find no cause until one asked her some personal questions and learned the ailment had started just after she learned that her maid had venereal disease, and she had become afraid of contracting it.

Hives, or what doctors call urticaria, are raised, itching welts that appear suddenly on the skin, usually on chest or abdomen, either singly or in several places at once. They are caused by the local release of histamine. They vary in size, sometimes being as small as pinheads. A welt usually remains for a few hours and then disappears as quickly as it came, possibly to reappear somewhere else. Occasionally hives can continue intermittently for many months. Most people who get them have a history of asthma or hay fever as well.

The allergens that cause hives are usually either foods such as shellfish, eggs, strawberries, chocolate, nuts, or mushrooms, or medications such as penicillin, other antibiotics, and even aspirin.

But hypersensitivity to cold, heat, or sunlight can result in hives. Or a welt may appear when the skin is injured in some way, perhaps scratched by someone's fingernail accidentally.

Psychiatrists have observed that attacks of urticaria often occur after a patient has felt fear or anger. For instance, a twenty-eight-year-old man suffered for eight years from urticaria. He himself had noticed that an attack came immediately after he experienced annoyance at some happening. He was admitted to a hospital for tests. One of them included an experiment in which he was falsely accused on two occasions of some irregularity by a nurse. At each accusation he became very upset. Within a few minutes, an urticarial rash broke out.

To prove again the power of suggestion on the unconscious part of the mind and also the power of the unconscious mind, in one experiment a cross was drawn with a pencil on both arms of a man under hypnosis. The suggestion was given him that when he awoke an urticarial wheal would develop within two hours at the designated spot of the cross on the left arm, but the right arm would remain normal. An hour after he was awakened from the hypnotic spell, the wheal formation on the left arm began to form. His right arm remained undisturbed.

Studies have shown that in urticaria, there may be a held-back, dependent longing for a parent symbolized by the "weeping" of the skin. Patients with urticaria usually are unable to cry. During therapy, as they regain the ability to weep, the urticaria clears up. After all, the extra fluid secretion by the skin is a kind of "weeping."

One woman recently came to me for consultation about a severe case of hives which refused to clear up in spite of medication. Her doctor did not know what caused the skin condition to persist. Her eyes looked red, as though she had been weeping. She was forty-four years old, apparently married, for she wore a wedding ring, and had a slim athletic figure and a pert little face.

Noting her reddened eyes, I asked whether she had been crying.

She said, "You're a good detective. Yes. Quite a bit lately."

"Do you want to tell me why?"

"My husband suddenly decided he wanted a divorce. It came like a bolt from the blue. I never suspected it. He said he had fallen in love with his secretary five years ago and thought he could give her up but now realized that was impossible. He asked me to give him a divorce."

"How do you feel about it?"

"Like I'd been struck by lightning. I'll give him the divorce, of course. He knows I wouldn't want him to stay with me if he was in love with another woman. But I've done a lot crying."

"Even through your skin," I observed.

"What do you mean?"

"The hives give off that moist quality that psychoanalysts describe as a kind of 'weeping' skin," I explained.

I saw her for several months. During her sessions with me she sobbed her heart out over the loss of her husband. The hives cleared up almost immediately, but there was still the problem of permitting her to express her grief and rage. For when a husband walks out of a marriage, the wife involved frequently goes through a mourning process which includes anger, sorrow, and, finally, acceptance of the loss.

When my patient ended her therapy, she was experiencing much less grief and slowly getting her life-style back on a normal level. In fact, she had begun to date a man she had met at a dinner party at a friend's home. She hinted to me that she thought the man was falling in love with her, and I detected a note of hopeful anticipation in her voice and expression when she told me about it. Though I have not seen her since that time, I am reasonably certain that she was able to work out a relationship with him once her divorce was finalized.

Dermatitis is an inflammation of the skin in which redness, blistering, oozing, or crusting occurs. Today the ailment called eczema is synonymous with chronic dermatitus. There are several varieties of dermatitis that even a dermatologist may find difficult to differentiate. Some have been associated with allergy. The common skin allergy is contact dermatitis. The Allergy Foundation of America recently estimated that about 600,000 working men and women have contact dermatitis arising from their occupations.

The skin is constantly replacing itself. Each day, billions of dead cells are shed and billions of new cells are formed. At home and at work the skin is exposed to all kinds of irritants, and normally it is able to resist their harmful effects. But certain people, after frequent exposure to certain substances or foods, come down with chronic dermatitis.

Psychiatrists have discovered that eczema and a skin disease known as psoriasis are usually caused by emotional conflicts. The allergy, if there is one, constitutes the conscious reason given for the skin condition. But in addition, there are unconscious reasons. One of them is the wish to masturbate, expressed through the scratching and continual self-touching of the rash. Underneath this lies the wish for love, the feeling "If nobody else loves me (touches me), I can at least love (touch) myself." Even the putting on of ointment is a touch, a modicum of self-love.

As the lives of those who suffer from eczema and psoriasis are studied, they show an infancy that held deep maternal deprivation. One woman, whose mother had died when she was two and a half years old, had never really known "a mother's touch." She was compensating for this lack of an essential in psychosexual growth by always scratching herself. The symptom showed her endless complaint to the world, "No one ever loved me and I must love myself."

There are undemonstrative mothers who create in the child a great hunger for a stroking and cuddling they never receive. The child may suffer an outbreak of skin disorder that shows the lack of physical contact in his early life. He now tries to get attention by means of infantile exhibitionism in a sublimated effort to induce adults to touch and cuddle him.

Outbreaks of the skin combine a variety of hidden emotions,

including rejection, guilt, masochism, a deep desire to receive physical expression of love from others, and exhibitionism. The skin, because it is the surface of the body, is the somatic expression of exhibitionism.

One woman, who had occasional outbreaks of acne, confessed during one analytic session that she had always wanted to be a striptease dancer.

"Why?" I asked, all the while admitting to myself that with her slim, curved figure, beautiful facial features, and streaming blond hair, she would indeed have made a seductive dancer.

"I loved to dance for my mother and father as a child," she said. "I would put on the radio and dance around the room and they would applaud. Later I took ballet lessons. But then when I went to college, I decided to become a social worker instead."

"That's a far cry from a striptease dancer," I observed.

She laughed. "It sure is. But in my heart I'm still yearning to be a striptease dancer. Even though I know, in the words of that popular song, 'It's Too Late, Baby.' "

"A dancer exhibits her body, whereas a social worker exhibits her mind," I observed. "Did you ever consider the possibility that your acne attacks are a way of expressing your wish to exhibit your body? Don't forget that was a very strong wish in your childhood and adolescence."

She thought about that. She said, "I sure did love to dance for my father! There's nobody to dance for anymore, now that he's dead."

"When did he die?" I asked.

"When I was nineteen," she answered. "I think it was about that time I gave up the idea of being any kind of dancer."

"But, as you say, in your heart you're still dancing," I said.

During her year of therapy she spoke many times of her repressed yearning to fling her body around the room as a dancer does, a yearning she had stifled at the death of her father. I said to her one day, "You can still become a dancer if you wish."

She laughed. "No. I'm resigned to a career of social work."

During the period of her therapy she experienced no acne outbreaks. The reason was that she was expressing feelings she had bottled up over the years so that there was no need for them to emerge via the surface of her skin. She had never married, but she suddenly met a young social worker whom she liked very much and told me one day he had proposed and she wanted time to think about whether she would marry him. Several weeks later she decided to go ahead with the marriage, and it was then she left therapy.

Sexual impulses, when unconsciously directed toward parts of the body, result in the feeling of guilt. For instance, in the scratching that is a substitute for masturbating, the person relieves his sexual tension, but he also inflicts pain upon himself because of his guilt. One patient described the feeling he got from scratching as "a vicious kind of pleasure." It is sadistic pleasure, a pleasure that, because of the guilt associated with it, also contains pain from an attack on one's own body.

A sixteen-year-old girl was sent to me by her family physician because she had a severe case of acne on her face that would not respond to routine medical treatment. She was dark-haired, very slight, and exceptionally pretty in spite of the rash on her face. She talked in a soft voice, one I could hardly hear. She seemed afraid of her very shadow.

I encouraged her to speak about her experiences. I asked her about the boys she went out with, how often she dated, and if there was any particular kind of boy she admired.

She said in almost a whisper, "I guess I'm what you would call popular. I always have a lot of dates. Sometimes it's hard to choose between three or four boys who want a date for the same evening."

"How do you feel about dating when your face is broken out?" I asked.

"It isn't *always* broken out," she said indignantly, in a much louder voice.

"Oh. I thought the acne was persistent," I said.

"There are lots of times I don't have one pimple on my skin," she said proudly.

"Could there be a connection between the time your skin is clear and the boy you are dating?" I asked.

She thought for a moment as her pretty face looked slightly pained. Then she said, "When I want to go out with a boy very much, when I feel very attracted to him, it seems that's the very time my face breaks out! As though to make sure I won't look my best. Isn't that a nuisance?"

"And when you have dates with boys you don't care so much about, your face remains clear?"

"Exactly. Isn't it strange?"

Not so strange. It was obvious that when she had a sexual conflict, when she felt very attracted to a boy and afraid she might give in to her desires, she unconsciously made herself look as unattractive as possible, as though to ward off any desire to act. If there was no sexual threat, if she did not feel particularly attracted to the boy, there would be no need for an outbreak of acne.

I did not explain this to her at once, but drew her out more about her experiences with her mother and father and older brother.

Her parents had always favored her brother, she thought, so that she grew up feeling inferior and unwanted. Her mother, particularly, granted her son favors she refused her daughter, claiming a girl had to be restricted more. She recalled that her brother had received a bicycle when he was ten but she had to wait until she was thirteen before her mother would allow her one. She was inwardly very jealous of her brother, though outwardly she loved him very much.

When her skin first started to break out, her brother taunted her with, "No boy will want to take you out looking like that," and she had always remembered his remark with a hurt feeling.

As she learned to release her feelings of resentment about being a girl and give up the fantasy that boys had it easier than girls in life, she stopped being jealous of her brother. She also discovered that her skin no longer broke out.

Dr. Franz Alexander noted that masochistic tendencies have a close affinity to the skin. He cited Dr. Joseph V. Klauder as saying, "The psyche exerts a greater influence on the skin than any other organ. . . . The skin is an important organ of expression of emotions comparable only to the eye."

Dr. Klauder pointed out that tattoos had significance because they were pictorial representations etched into the body to tell of desires on the part of the one who is tattooed. He also mentioned "stigmas of the crucifixion" (nails driven through the skin of the body) as a possible fantasy in the minds of those whose skin became disturbed.

Little children are prone to show off their bodies to win the attention and love of parents and playmates. Generally, exhibitionism may be used as a weapon in various forms of competition, but the process does bring with it a concomitant feeling of guilt. According to the talion principle (which states that the punishment should fit the nature and extent of the crime), the human skin, which serves as the outward means of exhibitionism, unconsciously becomes the site of a painful affliction whenever too much guilt is present. Psychoanalytic studies demonstrate that there is usually a hostile impulse involved in scratching. Because of the presence of guilt feelings in the afflicted individual, the hostile impulse is deflected from its original target (the mother and father of childhood) and centered against the self.

Dr. John Speigel, of Boston, president of the American Psychiatric Association, when he was practicing in Chicago, reported to the Chicago Institute for Psychoanalysis on the case of a twenty-two-year-old girl referred for treatment because of recurrent bouts of severe nervous skin outbreaks.

The lesions, which occurred mostly on her face and upper and lower extremities, were eczematoid in type, consisting of discrete, red, raw, itching areas. She scratched the lesions furiously, especially when she was asleep, "until they wept and bled, so that she was often quite disfigured." She had seen a number of dermatologists and had been told she could not be helped because the condition was due to emotional factors.

She had suffered from lesions on and off all her life. She had developed eczema a week after her birth. Her mother had been very disturbed during the pregnancy by the accidental death of her seven-year-old son and then by the desertion of her husband, who later divorced her. The girl spent her childhood in the homes of various relatives where she always felt insecure because of her mother's depreciated status as someone receiving charity.

The girl was shy and socially backward in high school but intelligent and alert in her studies. She suffered, feeling "different" and unwanted because of the eczema and the lack of a father and normal life. But in college, with physical maturity, she became popular socially.

After graduation she found a good job and began to form intense attachments to a number of men. But she always broke off the attachments with the appearance of a severe attack of eczema. When this recurrent pattern threatened her job and her relations with men, she had enough awareness to seek psychoanalytic treatment.

Almost at once, in the analysis she developed "an explosive masochistic transference neurosis." She demonstrated in every way that she expected to be rejected by the therapist, and she felt guilty because of both her hostile and her erotic transference feelings. These feelings she displaced to a series of men. She would gratify her sexual impulses, then become depressed and guilty and angry when she learned the man had no intention of marrying her. It was at this point that the skin lesions reached their height.

In the course of her analysis it became clear that the patient turned to the therapist, or some other man, as her long-lost father. To these father substitutes she showed a dependent oral craving and the wish for warm, cozy "cuddling." Frustrated in these wishes, she reacted with hostility and guilt. These feelings she handled partly by projection of the blame in the formula "all men are bastards," and partly by expressing her emotions in the skin eruptions. She expressed her hostile feelings by scratching; the resulting disfigurement represented her shame, humiliation, and rejection.

At this point, feeling completely unlovable, the patient would attempt to reestablish a closer relation to her mother. When this failed, she became very depressed. The cycle was brought to a close with the appearance of her hidden wish to be a man, as she paid more attention to her job, turned away from close ties to both women and men, felt a lightening of emotional anguish, and evidenced a clearing of the skin.

During three years of treatment she slowly developed insight into her repetitive pattern. Her skin lesions disappeared. Eventually she was able to form a more mature relationship with a man she ultimately married. With the reduction of guilt and hostility, she was able to allow herself to enjoy a man and take pleasure in sexual intimacy, rather than using it as a child would—to cuddle close to a mother or father.

The fact that her skin lesions had vanished showed she had lost her excessive need for childhood cravings she had never understood. As she could become aware of them, and express her feelings about her lost father and a mother she felt had demeaned herself, she was able to accept a maturity she had never known.

12

PREVENTION OF ILLNESS

" 'Tis the mind that makes the body rich," said Petruchio to Kate in *The Taming of the Shrew*. A mind with a positive attitude can go far toward avoiding illness, both mental and physical, as well as to help cure disease.

If we feel optimistic about life, if there is a sense of well-being in our heart, such feelings aid in maintaining a level of good health. It is the depressed, complaining person who is usually ill (which then gives him something he may complain about consciously, not realizing that the deeper reasons for his complaints are hidden from him). This type of individual usually has few friends, for no one likes to be around someone who complains about his health all the time. There is no bigger bore.

A recent patient on her first visit admitted ruefully, "My friends got so sick of listening to me telling them about all my bodily ailments that they said to me rather nastily, 'Go tell it to a psychiatrist.' So that's why I'm here."

I *had* to listen, I was being paid to listen, but I was also being paid to help, which her friends were not.

A positive mental attitude does not mean the denial of physical disease or the existence of psychological difficulties, as a clown does (many clowns are extremely unhappy and suffer a variety of physical illnesses). A positive mental attitude means recognizing that life will hold difficulties no matter how happy you feel but that the difficulties can be solved by means of sound thinking and wise action, if action is required. The person with a positive mental attitude does not let temporary difficulties, be they physical or psychic, overwhelm him with a defeatist attitude. Rather, he tackles them with energy and considers all possibilities in arriving at their solution.

Many men and women possess this positive mental attitude and do not need help in acquiring it. They have built it up over the years, based on a sense of security in childhood and feeling loved and wanted by their parents. Others, who lacked this childhood security, find that reading books about self-understanding helps them gain insights they otherwise would never have had. They can then lead their lives with more ease and comfort.

Then there are those who have a minister, a family physician, or a good friend with whom they talk over their problems and receive valuable advice or suggestions that help them decide what to do in a difficult situation. Usually the advice given coincides with what they themselves believe is the best procedure to follow. It gives them the straw they need, so to speak, to be able to act.

Still others feel they need the help of a psychiatrist or psychoanalyst, that they cannot go it alone or do not want to depend on anyone except a trained observer of human behavior. The very fact that they are able to ask and receive help from a psychiatrist or psychoanalyst is a strong indication that they have a positive mental attitude about themselves. The one who is too afraid to ask for assistance may, instead, turn to excessive drinking, overeating, drugs, chain-smoking, or sexual promiscuity, or live like a hermit. Any one of these outlets for anxiety will only increase self-destructive tendencies, rather than help the individual gain a positive mental attitude.

You can think yourself sick, and conversely you can help think yourself well. The more knowledge you possess about yourself, the more positive and hopeful your attitudes will be toward yourself and life in general. For it is the unreal fears and rages and guilts that keep you in a negative frame of mind. If you cannot face those debilitating, strength-sapping emotions, you will keep on unconsciously punishing yourself for having them.

As you come to understand that fears, rages, and guilts are natural feelings belonging to all men, and that if you have exaggerated them you have done so because of the hurt in your life, you will no longer suffer anxiety. You are a human being and entitled to all the emotions everybody possesses in order to express how he feels.

As you face deeper feelings, you will find your entire attitude toward life changes. Life becomes a challenge, a pleasure, a journey to be enjoyed, rather than a suffering to be borne.

This comes through a positive mental attitude, one in which you understand and accept yourself. It is an understanding and acceptance that wise men through the ages have advised for each of us if we wish to feel fulfilled, to enjoy our capacities to their fullest potential.

I base my treatment not only on Freudian principles but on all psychoanalytic schools that play their part in understanding human nature. I am what is called eclectic, a psychoanalyst who uses —if practical—the methods of all schools. I have made it a particular specialty to employ short-term therapy in order to relieve the patient from his immediate suffering.

I believe it is important to reduce immediate anxiety so a patient's mental outlook will be more positive and make him more amenable to searching for an appraisal and analysis of the cause of his illness and its consequences. Then he will be able to apply his rational mind to the cure of his psychic and physical ailments.

It is interesting that during therapy a person seems to become more positive as he feels he can change through acquiring and using new insights about his behavior. He relates his current behavior to that of the past, and understands how and why he has felt tormented. The process of understanding the self is not comparable to getting a new life, but rather to becoming able to use abilities that lay dormant because of inner fear, rage, and guilt.

Usually if someone has a long, deep-seated physical illness, you will find a history of psychic conflicts and inner hangups in his life. It would be utopia if he had been able to solve those conflicts early in life and thus avoid the physical illness. But this is fantasy, at least at this stage of acceptance of the importance of emotions by the world—though emotions are slowly becoming more accepted as a cause of most physical illness. As more and more awareness takes place, people will be able, far earlier in their lives, to understand that certain physical and psychological symptoms indicate that inner conflicts are causing distress.

What are some of these symptoms?

In children: excessive lying, truancy, failing in classes, withdrawal at home and at school, lack of playmates, excessive temper tantrums, perpetual tardiness, always being early, bed-wetting beyond the age of three or four, excessive craving for food, especially sweets. And, of course, continual catching of colds or constant suffering from any other bodily ailment such as diarrhea or constipation, coughing, or insomnia.

In adults: alcoholism, drug addiction, absenteeism from work, the compulsion to overwork, the tendency to suffer frequent accidents, the urge to promiscuity, the need *not* to get married and have children, overeating, undereating, smoking to the point of being plagued by coughing spasms, and suffering from one bodily ailment after another.

If you feel pain in any part of your body, whether a sudden acute pain or a chronic symptom that will not disappear, you should seek an immediate checkup by a physician to make sure you do not need medication or surgery. If nothing is organically wrong and the pain persists, you would be well advised to see a psychiatrist or psychoanalyst who will help you explore the inner conflicts that may be contributing to your psychic and physical tension.

What if you cannot afford someone who may charge fees that are beyond your means? Throughout the nation there are mental health community clinics whose staff people are trained to help you find therapy at a price you can afford. There is great need today, because of the demand, for even more of such services, and it is expected that under the coming National Health Insurance program—probably to be established within the next ten years—mental health services will expand. The great need is for trained personnel to give effective therapy.

If, in addition to having physical complaints, you feel very depressed and the depression has led to alcoholism or drug addiction, you would be wise to secure psychological help. I have known a number of men and women alcoholics who, after therapy, cease drinking and add years to their lives, not to mention the fact that they are happier years. You cannot have a psychological problem that does not have some effect on your body, just as you cannot suffer a bodily injury without its affecting your mind.

A thirty-nine-year-old architect walked into my office, sent by his doctor because he drank to excess. He was a very handsome man, looking rather like Cary Grant, with a casual, happy-go-lucky manner. His doctor had told me that this man was married to a beautiful and wealthy woman who was tremendously concerned about his drinking and what it was doing to their lives and the life of their eight-year-old daughter.

He was one of the many who try to find refuge in liquor, rather than in meeting life's daily confrontations. I needed only thirty minutes' conversation with him to realize that this handsome, outwardly successful man considered himself a complete failure. As he told me frankly, "My wife is adorable and wealthy, yet I feel I am failing her by not being much of a success as an architect. I live on her money, rather than my own. She depends on me to make her happy and I try. But much of the time I feel I can't make myself happy, let alone her."

"Nobody should ask another person to 'make' him happy," I said. "Happiness comes from within the self."

"I agree!" His voice was enthusiastic. "And I'm here to find out why I have to drink and put myself in a state of oblivion to feel happy."

"Perhaps because you don't feel capable of facing life's pains and pleasures without alcohol," I said.

"It's just that after three drinks, nothing can touch me," he said. "I'm beyond the reach of anyone. In my own world. Completely by myself."

"But that isn't a very responsible attitude, is it?" I asked.

"No," he said. "And I'm the first to admit that I cop out on responsibility when the going gets tough. It isn't that I don't love my wife and daughter. I do. Very much. But life just becomes too much for me at times."

Alcoholics are difficult to treat because the habit becomes so ingrained that they put up all kinds of resistance to giving up liquor. Periods ranging from many months to several years are required for them to gain enough understanding of the unconscious reasons why they drink so they are able to drink more moderately or give it up completely.

This man was not willing to invest the time, or his wife's money, to find out the reasons that drove him to excessive drinking. He left after the first session, saying, "Someday, if I earn enough on my own, I'll be back." Six years later he came back and went through psychotherapy successfully.

One woman in her late fifties, who had started to drink heavily after her divorce, came to me for consultation and assistance. She was independently wealthy, having inherited money from both her parents. They were parents who had taken care of her financially but had brought her up, as an only child, to feel emotionally rejected, always placing their needs first. She had felt guilty about any pleasure she allowed herself, in spite of her money. Abruptly confronted with the fact that she now had to live alone, she started to drink excessively.

When she came to me for help, she had just met a man in his late fifties, who was also divorced and also quite wealthy. She fell in love and wanted the romance to result in marriage. She realized she faced a severe problem in trying to stop her alcoholism and thus took action. After a few months of therapy she began to

understand the reasons for her excessive drinking, which was in
a way a kind of self-punishment.

She came to realize that her parents were selfish, punitive
people who had never given her much love. She had always
blamed herself for their rejection. Now she understood how she
had idolized selfish, shallow parents. She was able to start to think
for herself, to accept that she was entitled to her share of pleasure
in life, rather than constant punishment.

She told me that her fiancé (he had proposed) drank even more
than she. She brought him to one session, trying to persuade him
to accept help. He stumbled into the office so drunk he could
hardly sit upright in the chair, much less make sense when he
talked. He refused to return, insisting he could help himself; he
didn't need "any lady psychiatrist" to tell him what to do.

The woman managed to stop drinking even though he did not.
But she married him anyhow. They moved out of New York to
a ranch in Wyoming. At least she was able to give up her alcoholism and help him manage himself better.

Drug addiction represents another way to try to get away from
painful feelings. Only someone with deep conflicts becomes a
drug addict. Both alcoholism and drug addiction also unconsciously serve as rationalization for the man who is sexually afraid.
Both reduce the potency of the man who is frightened of sexual
feelings. They give him an excuse for not performing. In some
cases, they furnish the excuse to carry through on homosexual
impulses as inhibitions fail, as they are known to do under the
influence of alcohol and drugs. Many a homosexual says, "I didn't
know what I was doing last night, I was so drunk," as though this
will explain his aberrant sexual behavior.

I have never encountered a case of alcoholism or drug addiction
where the underlying problems were not emotional. The person
who cripples himself by excessively drinking or taking drugs is
running away from the agonizing conflicts in his life, rather than
solving them. He is copping out, adding anguish to the already
existing anguish in his existence by taking on new, destructive

habits, for both may produce crippling physical illnesses as well as psychic degeneration. Alcoholism may lead to liver diseases and the destruction of brain cells.

We are just starting to appreciate and understand the terrifying influence of drugs on the entire body, as well as alcohol, including the affect on the fetus a mother may be bearing. Physicians in Seattle, Washington, recently identified a pattern of serious birth defects among children born to women who are chronic alcoholics.

With an estimated two million alcoholic women in the nation, at least half of whom are of childbearing age, the finding is expected to have far-reaching significance even if it relates only to very heavy alcohol consumption, according to a story in the *New York Times* on July 3, 1973, by Jane E. Brody. Miss Brody reported that the malformation syndrome, described in the journal *Lancet,* involved an overall growth deficiency, lagging intellectual and motor development, small head size, heart defects, and subtle facial and limb abnormalities.

Eight children in the Seattle study (several more have since been studied elsewhere) all had subnormal intelligence with I.Q.'s ranging from less than 50 to 83, and most were below average for their age in performance of physical activity. At birth they weighed only half of what the average baby weighs and were about 20 percent shorter than average. They continued to be retarded in growth after birth.

The children studied were all unrelated and came from three ethnic groups, American Indian, black, and white. All they had in common was a mother who was an alcoholic during pregnancy. The study was conducted by Drs. Kenneth L. Jones, David W. Smith, Christy N. Ulleland, and Ann P. Streissguth, of the Department of Pediatrics at the University of Washington in Seattle. It was an outgrowth of Dr. Ulleland's observation that children born to alcoholic mothers tended to suffer growth deficiency and delay in development.

The authors concluded: "The data are sufficient to establish that maternal alcoholism can cause serious aberrant fetal development. Further studies are warranted relative to the more specific cause and prevention of this tragic disorder."

It is not known how chronic alcohol consumption can produce such an effect on the developing fetus. Dr. Smith suggested several possibilities. He said, "It could be a direct toxic effect of the alcohol, or the effect of a breakdown product of alcohol, or some other chemical in the alcoholic beverage, or it could be the indirect result of an effect on the mother's nutrition or biochemistry, such as a vitamin deficiency."

He believes, however, that simple malnutrition, which is characteristic of alcoholics, is not the whole story, since ordinary maternal malnutrition usually does not affect the length of the fetus and prenatally malnourished infants tend to catch up in growth after birth.

What is known is that alcohol readily crosses the placenta so that the alcohol consumed by the mother reaches the fetus moments later. Studies in monkeys have shown that alcohol levels in the fetal tissues may be as great as ten times higher than those in the mother's tissues.

Included in our discussion of physical pain, there is one kind of pain that seems to have no apparent cause but that therapy can help. A very interesting report recently came from the Veterans Administration Center at San Diego, California, revealing that therapy was effective with men who suffered a bodily pain that could not be eased by drugs or surgery.

For instance, according to an article by Stuart Auerbach in the *Washington Post* of June 14, 1973, John W. Sawyer, a Korean War veteran and ex-policeman, felt pain all the time in his right leg, as if "someone's shoving a hot poker from the hips down the back of my leg." And Ralph Fish, another veteran, had suffered from a "bad back" for twenty-five years, though he worked as a laborer to support his family until finally he could not stand on his feet.

Authorities estimate that more than seven million Americans

suffer from what is believed to be "untreatable" back pains, the most common type of pain. Others suffer from unexplained headaches that are severe enough to keep them home from work. Still others complain of the "phantom-limb pain," a constant ache that seems to come from an arm or leg that has been amputated.

Most of those with "untreatable" pain become chronic invalids. But the center in San Diego is among the few places that are trying to help those with a pain who cannot be treated medically or by surgery. Chronic pain appears to be caused by the same stimulation of the sensory nerve fibers as normal pain, but for unexplained reasons it persists, resisting all medical treatment.

The psychological treatment at the center has made it possible for a number of the veterans to leave the hospital and return to their families and to work. Says Dr. Richard A. Sternbach, the psychologist who runs the pain unit, "I'm teaching the patients to live with their pain. They know I can't take it away. As a consequence they learn to feel that the pain isn't so great." He tries to help them master their pain and lead as close to a normal life as possible.

Dr. Sternbach thinks that the statistics of the first eleven months of the pain unit (which opened in May, 1972) have proved that his method works. Of sixty patients in the unit, only fifteen were helped with surgery. On entering the unit, the average score on the "pain scale" was sixty-two, even though many veterans were taking drugs. On leaving, with their drug intake sharply cut, they rated their pain twenty points lower.

Dr. Sternbach refuses to reward pain. If a patient complains about pain to a nurse, she looks away, yawns, and pays no attention. Medication is given at regularly scheduled times, not when a patient complains of pain. Patients are encouraged to exercise, work at odd jobs in the hospital, and take occupational therapy. Then the nurses praise them for taking action. The treatment also includes daily group therapy sessions at which Dr. Sternbach lectures on the physiology of pain. He also tries to withdraw the medication gradually from patients.

"This treatment has made the difference between being able to be a productive individual or having to apologize because you're lying around at home while others are earning wages," he says. "The pain makes you afraid you are not a man anymore."

This is what psychiatrists call the "secondary gains" of illness. It may be used as an excuse for further escape from painful conflicts, for retreat from the world of reality either temporarily or permanently in the case of the disabled veterans. There were men who had physical defects to start with but who were allowing their psychic conflicts to intensify bodily pain, which they then used as an escape from functioning in society. Dr. Sternbach did not permit them to indulge in self-pity. He treated them as whole men.

Actually, if these veterans could receive more intensive psychological help, they might find their pain disappearing altogether and their lives changed drastically. However, Dr. Sternbach's work is a step in the right direction. Each man is encouraged to feel he is being paid special attention and in some measure is being helped to achieve a new sense of identity, rather than left to his own misery in an attempt to escape life's eternal conflicts.

Conflicts there will always be. One needs the strength and confidence to face them, not run away from them.

When we try to escape the powerful drives that motivate our sexual and aggressive activity, we cause ourselves further pain. Only by becoming aware of the emotions that revolve around these conflicts do we ease the pain that is all too often both physical and psychic.

What about those who refuse to seek help though their inner troubles stick out, to others, like the proverbial sore thumb? We all know people who say scornfully, "I can run my life by myself —I don't need anyone's help," though the record shows they have not been very successful in achieving a happy life.

It is very difficult to persuade someone who is convinced otherwise that he should go to a psychiatrist or psychoanalyst when he feels depressed, is drinking too much, overworks, or is always suffering some minor physical ailment. He prefers to continue to suffer, because of an inner guilt, rather than relieve his suffering, both physical and mental. In such instances you have to honor his preference even though he may eventually destroy himself.

Today, however, more and more persons are seeking the assistance of the experts as they realize body and mind are one. They know they cannot separate their physical functions from their psychic activity, and that the healthier the one is, the healthier the other will be.

If there is one point I am trying to make in this book, perhaps it is the importance of knowing and understanding your feelings. We have to hide, from ourselves, many of our powerful, inner emotions. If we are able to become aware of them, realize they are natural and normal, and not feel guilty about them, we will be far happier. Instead of being driven by these hidden emotions, we must control them consciously. By so doing we will no longer have to tie up precious psychic energy trying to keep them concealed from the world about us but, more importantly, from ourselves.

I know, from the many patients I have seen over the years, the destructive effect on the mind and the body of hidden anger, hidden fear, hidden jealousy, hidden grief. As the anger, the fear, the jealousy, the grief are able to register in the patient's consciousness, it is as though a veritable flood of feeling bursts forth, followed by a deep sense of calm and confidence. As the patient realizes how needlessly guilty he has felt, usually over fantasies, an ease and accommodation in his life-style result.

As one woman, after bringing her inner conflicts to light and exercising them, said, "I feel as though a deep infection inside me had suddenly cleared up and I was healthy once more, like I felt as a child."

It is these feelings of fear, guilt, and hidden rage that contribute to and cause many of our physical complaints. And it is a proven fact that physical illnesses clear up in patients whose psyches have become freed of long-buried conflicts.

There is still nothing wiser than the advice given by the ancient Greek oracle at Delphi: "Know thyself." We might add, "In depth."

INDEX